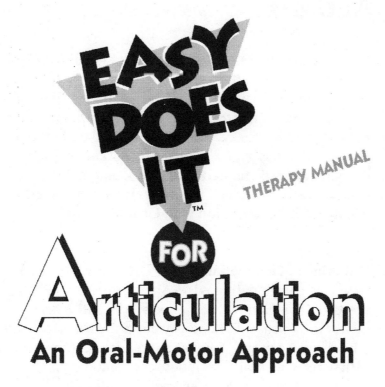

EASY DOES IT

THERAPY MANUAL

FOR Articulation

An Oral-Motor Approach

Robin Strode
Catherine Chamberlain

Skill:	oral-motor
Ages:	4 - 12

Copyright © 1997 LinguiSystems, Inc.

LinguiSystems, Inc.
3100 4th Avenue
E. Moline, IL 61244-9700
1-800 PRO IDEA
1-800 776-4332

ISBN 0-7606-0144-5

About the Authors

Robin M. Strode, M.A., CCC-SLP, has had over 20 years experience as a speech-language pathologist. She has been in private practice for 15 years. In addition to her private practice, Robin has served as a school consultant and part-time instructor in the Communication Disorders Department at the University of Kentucky. She formerly worked in the public schools for eight years. Robin has special interest in working with preschool and early elementary-aged children with developmental delays, language disorders, and/or speech disorders. *Easy Does It for Articulation: An Oral-Motor Approach* is Robin's fifth publication with LinguiSystems.

Catherine E. Chamberlain, M.A., CCC-SLP, has had 25 years experience as a speech-language pathologist. She maintains a private practice serving the preschool population. Catherine works at the Early Childhood Development Center in Winchester, Kentucky and she formerly worked in the public schools for 14 years. She has special interest in working with students with autism, mental disabilities, and multiple handicaps. *Easy Does It for Articulation: An Oral-Motor Approach* is Catherine's seventh publication with LinguiSystems.

January 1997

Dedication

To our parents, Pat and Harry Miller and Mildred Ellison, who have been a constant source of love, strength, courage, and inspiration.

To all the professionals who have been so generous in sharing their knowledge and expertise with us, especially Mariana D'Amico, Occupational Therapist extraordinaire.

As always, to our wonderful families. Thanks for all the support and encouragement: Tom, Cole, Chris, and Murphy.

And to Lauri Whiskeyman and all our friends at LinguiSystems who have made writing and learning a pleasure.

Illustrations by Paul Dallgas-Frey, Margaret Warner, Beth Ducey, and Ken Prestley

Table of Contents

Introduction

Easy Does It For Articulation: An Oral-Motor Approach is designed to facilitate development of the motor skills needed for speech sound production through sensorimotor and oral-motor intervention. This enables the child to develop motor skills for speech and motor memory of speech sound productions so he can acquire appropriate movement and placement of the articulators for the target sounds. He can then put the target sounds in units and more complex environments.

The program is divided into sound groups that are produced with similar articulatory movements or placements. Each sound group chapter begins by preparing the child's entire body to organize for speech. It then progresses through preparing the speech mechanism via face wake-up activities, vocal warm-ups, and taste and food activities that can facilitate the target articulatory placements.

Children who may benefit from this program are those of all ages and levels of severity, including those who:

- ◆ have an articulation or phonological disorder.

- ◆ have difficulty achieving or stabilizing phoneme production for individual or multiple sounds, or sound classes.

- ◆ lack awareness of the articulators and articulatory placement, or who have difficulty following auditory and visual directions.

- ◆ have underlying oral-motor problems contributing to their speech disorder. These can result in inconsistent progress, or a lack of progress in therapy.

- ◆ have gross or fine motor problems along with their speech disorder.

- ◆ lose intelligibility in more complex phonetic environments.

- ◆ have Down Syndrome or other conditions with low muscle tone.

- ◆ have a hearing impairment. The program can facilitate articulator placement and feedback.

- ◆ have sensory problems in the oral area.

- ◆ have difficulty organizing the system for speech.

- ◆ have a diagnosis of developmental verbal apraxia or dysarthria.

- ◆ have difficulty achieving production of the /er/ or /l/ sound.

- ◆ have a persistent frontal or lateral lisp.

Specific oral-motor facilitation techniques are provided to help the child develop better oral-motor control, precision, strength, and coordination to achieve and stabilize target placement and movement for sound production. Troubleshooting ideas are included for additional help.

Easy Does It For Articulation: An Oral-Motor Approach is a complete program for implementing a sensorimotor-based approach to articulation therapy. The *Therapy Manual* includes:

◆ an overview of the total program with explanations of each component, including the rationale for use

◆ program guidelines and suggestions

◆ illustrated techniques for body positioning and oral-motor facilitation

◆ suggestions for creating an oral-motor materials box

◆ a classroom program with sample lesson plans

◆ a tracking sheet for oral-motor stimulation that can be used for therapy planning and record keeping (one in each chapter)

◆ a tracking sheet for speech practice that may be used as a lesson plan and as a record of progress

◆ answers to common questions

◆ sound group chapters organized by articulator placement that include direct oral-motor facilitation techniques

◆ reference list

The *Materials Book* includes:

◆ worksheets for practice on consonant phonemes in isolation; syllables; initial, final, and medial positions of words; multisyllabic words; and phrases and sentences

◆ word pictures of each consonant phoneme in initial, medial, and final positions of words and multisyllabic words

◆ hand signal pictures and descriptions that can be used to cue consonant productions

This approach to articulation therapy can be combined with other treatment approaches. It can be used in a phonological approach to work on patterns of errors in cycles. It can be combined with treatment approaches for developmental verbal apraxia and dysarthria. It can be used to treat a single persistent sound error. The important thing to remember is to start where the child is and do what works to help him achieve normal speech skills.

Robin and Catherine

Program Sequence

Speech is a whole body process with many contributors to age-appropriate speech skills including respiration and breath support, body positioning; muscle tone; jaw strength, stability and grading; palate positioning, control and movement; tongue and lip positioning, strength, control, and movement; and vocal fold functioning. Speech can be influenced by a weakness, incoordination, or breakdown in any part of the system. The requisites for proficient speech production can be established by adequately preparing each part of the system prior to speech practice.

Easy Does It For Articulation: An Oral-Motor Approach uses sensorimotor techniques to sequentially prepare all parts of the communication system before speech tasks are attempted. This allows the child to successfully produce speech tasks that previously were difficult or impossible for him.

Each chapter includes the following:

a. **Whole Body Wake-Ups:** These are a brief warm-up of the body during gross motor activities to facilitate and promote alertness, organization, focus, calming, mobility, coordination, normal muscle tone, respiration/breath support, and cooperation. This warm-up gets all the systems revved to go, just as an engine is warmed up when starting a car. Movement helps provide stability and support for the various systems involved in speech production. Movement activities should precede oral-motor techniques, progressing from general to specific tasks, from the periphery of the body to the mouth.

b. **Body Positioning and Jaw Stability:** Properly align the child's hips, shoulders, head, and jaw to give his body a stable base for speech. From stability comes mobility, so the articulators can move independently with control, strength, and precision. Independent tongue action is needed for accurate production of many speech sounds, and jaw stability needs to be established before the tongue can move independently from the jaw. For all oral-motor, feeding, and speech tasks, it's important to have the child positioned correctly.

c. **Face Wake-Ups:** These are brief stimulation exercises for oral-motor preparation. Stimulation outside the mouth can help increase sensory awareness, normalize sensitivity and tone, and lead to control, strength, and precision of articulator movement. It's important to begin stimulation outside the mouth on the face, and then gradually go inside the mouth.

d. **Vocal Warm-Ups:** These are brief warm-up activities of the speech engine/mechanism using speech and other sounds. You can vary the warm-up by doing some in a sustained fashion, some quickly, some loudly, some quietly, some in a high pitch, some in a low pitch, some with a growl, and some with a whisper. Try different productions to make it fun. Be careful of activities that may strain the voice.

e. **Taste and Food Activities:** These activities provide a way to introduce stimulation inside the child's mouth which is less intrusive than the direct facilitation techniques that will follow. Food experiences can facilitate mouth wake-up, jaw grading and stability, muscle control, strength, mobility, precision, and normalized sensitivity. Never force food experiences on the child. **Always check for food allergies and sensitivities, particularly before using peanut products.**

f. **Direct Facilitation Techniques:** Direct stimulation to the child's articulators encourages sensory awareness, normalized tone and sensitivity, stability, muscle control, strength and precision, and coordination of movements. These techniques facilitate correct positioning, movement, and placement of the articulators for phoneme production. They are provided in each chapter specific to the speech sounds being targeted. Provide any facilitation the child needs to successfully achieve placement for the target phoneme.

Not all direct facilitation techniques need to be implemented. Each one used however, should be repeated three times. The child should then attempt the speech target. Always explain what you are going to do before beginning. With older children, you can explain the purpose of the techniques. Use a fun dialogue when introducing each technique to the child (i.e., "I'm going to tickle the front of your tongue"). Never force a child to accept oral-motor stimulation. See **Program Guidelines** on pages 10-12 if the child is resistant to oral-motor tasks. Techniques are included for:

◆ stability and gradation of the jaw

◆ closure, rounding, and retraction/spreading of the lips

◆ central groove, elevation, retraction, spreading, and protrusion of the tongue

A *Tracking Sheet for Oral-Motor Stimulation* for daily planning and record keeping is provided in each chapter. It has a summary of techniques for each sound group.

g. **Troubleshooting:** Ideas to deal with problems are given at the end of each chapter.

Speech Practice

Each chapter also includes speech practice worksheets. It's important to follow oral-motor intervention with a functional activity such as speech practice.

1. When introducing a speech sound, explain it to the child in terms he can understand. Describe articulator placements and movements, air flow requirements, and whether the vocal folds are vibrating.

2. Provide all cues needed for the child to successfully achieve speech goals including oral-motor facilitation techniques. Touch cues for each sound are included in each chapter and hand signals are found on pages 174-176 of the *Materials Book*.

3. Once placement is established, put the target consonant sound in a phonemic environment that facilitates correct sound placement and production. Suggestions are listed under **Tips and Troubleshooting** in each chapter.

4. A typical articulation therapy approach is recommended with this program, but other methods can be incorporated. A Van Riper-type sequence is useful to achieve consistency and stability

of production of the target sound in increasingly more difficult tasks. Begin with isolation, progress to syllables, word productions, multisyllabic words, then phrases and sentences. Adapt the program as needed for individual children. A phonological approach may be used once the child has established use of the sound at the word level. Our approach may be used with children with a diagnosis of developmental apraxia or dysarthria to establish consonant sound productions and to facilitate connected speech.

5. Worksheets specific to target sound productions are found in the *Materials Book*. Each chapter has a scene picture that incorporates words from target sound groups for phrase and sentence practice or for additional word practice. Word pictures for each phoneme in all applicable positions of words and multisyllabic words are also included on pages 135-173 in the *Materials Book*.

6. A reproducible tracking sheet for speech practice is included on page 28 for keeping records of daily therapy objectives and progress.

Program Guidelines

1. When implementing this program with a child, it's important to understand how his system works. It is helpful to have a good knowledge of the anatomy and physiology of the speech mechanism, particularly in the areas of respiration and breath support for speech, muscle tone, swallowing, feeding, oral-motor skills, articulation from a placement and motor basis, and tactile defensiveness and sensitivity in the face and oral area. A good evaluation should be conducted which observes these components over time during different tasks to delineate the child's areas of weakness that are contributing to the speech disorder. From this, a program can be designed to meet the child's specific needs.

2. Do an exam of the child's oral mechanism to make sure there are no physical contributors to the speech disorder such as enlarged tonsils or adenoids, allergies, structural abnormalities of the articulators, or a shortened lingual frenulum. Check the child's hearing.

3. Check the child's muscle tone to determine whether he has normal tone, high tone, low tone, or mixed tone in the body and oral area. Use caution implementing body, face, and oral-motor techniques on a child with high-tone. Consult with a pediatric OT or PT when appropriate to determine which activities or stimulations may be inappropriate for children with tactile sensitivity, high tone, mixed tone, or seizure disorders.

4. When implementing techniques, observe the child's responses for areas of weakness, lack of control or precision, reduced range of motion, over-sensitivity or reduced sensitivity to touch, and tone variations. Then, target these areas to normalize responses.

5. Work on a team when possible. Consult with a pediatric OT or PT when implementing a feeding or oral-motor program as needed.

6. Consult with the child's parents regarding food sensitivities and allergies (particularly for peanut products) before using foods in therapy with the child. Explain to them what is entailed in an oral-motor articulation program, why it will be implemented, and the target results.

7. Wear gloves and wash your hands well before and after working in a child's mouth. Check if the child has latex allergies before using latex gloves.

8. Determine if the child has normal sensitivity, hypersensitivity, or hyposensitivity in the oral area before beginning an oral-motor program. Reducing tactile defensiveness allows the child to accept working around and in the oral area during speech facilitation. Always follow oral-motor stimulation with a functional activity such as eating or speech practice.

9. Never force food or taste experiences on a child. If he rejects activities, it may be due to hypersensitivity and tactile defensiveness in the oral area. In this case, begin decreasing sensitivity away from the face. You will gradually work to the face and mouth. Start with texture experiences on the child's hands such as rubbing lotion on them, wiping them with a towel, finding toys hidden in beans/sand/pebbles, or finger painting with shaving cream.

Progress to the child's facial area and begin desensitizing outside the mouth. Wipe the child's face with a washcloth, rub with lotion, or pat and stroke it.

Then, desensitize inside the child's mouth. Introduce techniques slowly inside the mouth using slow movements with firm, deep pressure. Use an Infa-dent to stroke along the upper inner gum line from molar to molar three times. Then, use your thumb to exert downward pressure on the midline of the child's lower jaw (i.e., hook your thumb over the lower incisors and press down) for a few seconds. Use a gloved finger to maintain pressure for 3 to 5 seconds on the midline of the child's tongue. Stroke the roof of the child's mouth from front to back, being careful not to elicit a gag reflex. Consult with a professional trained in sensory/oral defensiveness prior to implementing these techniques as needed.

10. If a child is resistant to oral-motor tasks, slowly attempt to introduce these tasks in the following progression:

    a. Explain the technique to the child and tell him why you want to do it. Demonstrate it on yourself.

    b. Work on the whole body and face without any mouth work for a while. Implement a plan to desensitize the face and mouth area (See #9).

    c. Have the child perform the oral-motor activity on a doll or on you.

    d. Have the child watch you do the oral-motor technique with another child while you explain what you are doing and why you are doing it.

    e. Have the child do the technique on himself. Reward him with praise or a reinforcer.

    f. Briefly do the technique on the child once. Gradually increase the amount and frequency of the stimulation. Reward him with praise or a reinforcer.

11. It's important to correctly position the child's body for oral-motor stimulation and speech practice. Stability of the body and jaw allows for greater mobility so that movement may be skilled and precise. The child should be in 90°-90°-90° positioning (hips, knees, and ankles flexed at a 90-degree angle), sitting with her back straight and her feet flat on the floor or a footrest. The child's head should be in midline with her chin slightly tucked. Make sure the child's head is not tilted back with the chin up, as this posture encourages a tongue-forward position with the lips open.

The child may also lie prone on the floor, propped on her elbows with her elbows directly below her shoulders. The child's head should be forward and up, not sunk between the shoulders. The child's jaw may be resting on her cupped hands or fist to provide jaw stability if needed when she is sitting or lying. Remember, stability leads to mobility. A stable jaw allows the lips and tongue to move independently from jaw movements.

12. When applying stimulation to one side of the child's face, jaw, gums, lips, or tongue, always do the same to the other side. Symmetrical application of stimulation is important.

13. When implementing techniques to the body, face, and mouth, you want to use deep, firm pressure which can be used for desensitization or facilitation. Some children, however, may respond best to light pressure. Find out what works best for each specific child.

14. During resistance tasks with the child's jaw, lips, or tongue, make sure the child's back is straight and his head is in midline with his chin slightly tucked. Don't let the child's head move forward, backward, up, or down during stimulation as this defeats the purpose of the activity. The head will be doing the work rather than the articulator.

15. When doing direct facilitation techniques, make sure the child's mouth isn't open too wide. It should be in a neutral, open position whenever possible. Generally, the child's tongue should not be protruded during oral facilitation.

16. Use normal safety precautions when putting anything in the child's mouth. Materials should be clean and safe for the child's use. Clean oral-motor equipment with an antibacterial soap and rinse well. You can further clean with alcohol. Some items may be cleaned in the dishwasher on the top rack.

If you do not feel competent or at ease using the techniques in this program, confer with a professional trained in oral-motor intervention.

Illustrated Oral-Motor Techniques

Not all techniques are illustrated. A technique may fall under more than one heading because it may facilitate more than one position or movement. See each chapter for descriptions of the techniques.

Positioning

It's important to give the speech mechanism a stable base.

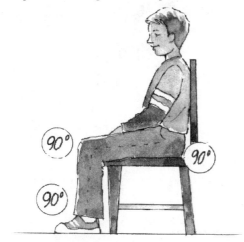

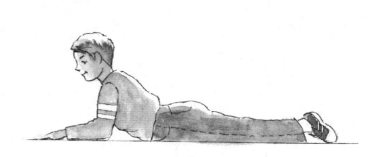

1. 90° - 90° - 90°
    hips, knees, and ankles at 90°;
    feet flat on floor

2. **prone on elbows**
    elbows directly under shoulders,
    head forward and up
    (not sunk between shoulders)

Face Wake-Ups

This is used to prepare the muscles of the face and mouth for speech production.

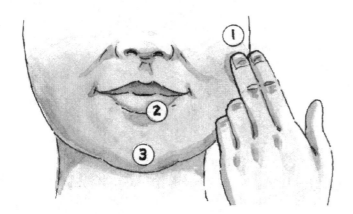

1. **face pats**
    Use two fingers to pat cheeks, lips, and chin.

a.   **b.**

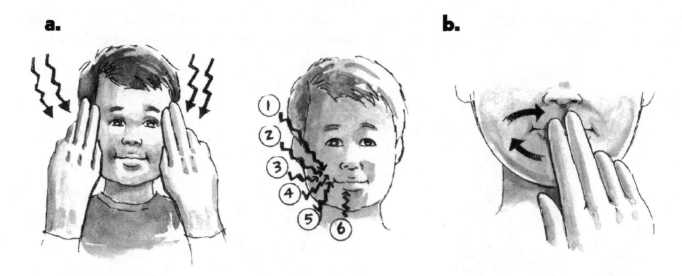

2. **manual vibration**
   Using your index and middle fingers, (a) vibrate along facial muscles from origin to point of insertion at mouth and (b) around lips.

Jaw Stability Techniques

Jaw stability and grading are important for all speech sounds, particularly for connected speech.

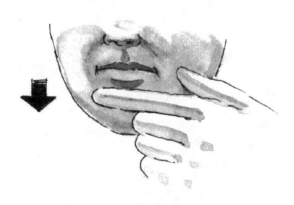   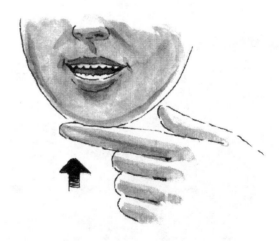

1. **resistance to jaw opening**
   Push down on the child's chin as he attempts to keep his mouth closed.

2. **resistance to jaw closing**
   Push upward on the child's chin while he attempts to keep his mouth open.

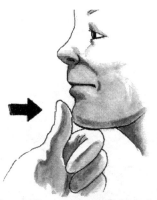

3. push into the point of the chin
Push inward on the point of the
child's chin.

4. bite block
Place an object between the
child's molars.

5. jaw cupping
Have the child cup his chin between
the palms of both hands with his fingers
along his jaw and his thumbs along or
behind the angle of the mandible.

Lip Closure Techniques

These techniques are important for /p, b/ and /m/ sounds. Lip closure can be affected by head and back
positioning, low tone, and enlarged tonsils and adenoids.

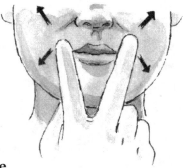

1. bunny nose
Place your index and middle fingers on
either side of the child's nose. Vibrate
down to the child's top lip. Hold briefly.

2. V-pressure
Place your index finger and middle finger
in a V above the child's lips. Push up and
out. For the bottom lip, push down and out.

15

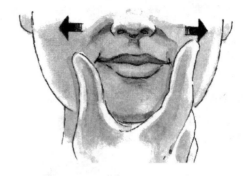

3. mustache press
Place your index finger on the area
above the child's top lip and press in.

4. lip stroke
Place your thumb and index finger
at the center of the child's lips.
Stroke to corners and hold briefly.

Lip Rounding/Protruding Techniques

These techniques are important for /w, sh, ch/ and /j/ sounds.

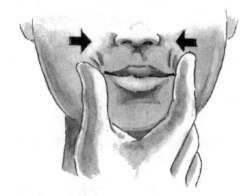

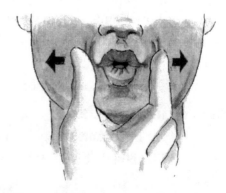

1. pucker resistance
Have the child smile or say "ee"
as you push his lips into a pucker.

2. smile resistance
Have the child pucker or say "ooh"
as you pull his lips into a smile.

16

Central Groove of the Tongue Techniques

These techniques are important for /s, z, sh, ch, j, er, r/ and /th/ sounds.

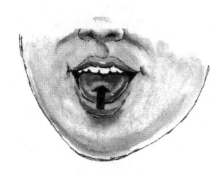

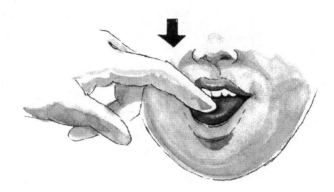

1. **central groove stroke**
   Stroke the central groove of the child's tongue from the tip to halfway back.

2. **central groove tap**
   Administer quick taps to the child's tongue along the central groove from the tip to halfway back.

Tongue Tip/Front Elevation and Spreading Techniques

These techniques are important for /t, d, n, l, s, z, sh, ch, j, er/ and /r/ sounds.

1. **tongue tip press: in**
   Press into the child's tongue tip. Repeat and have the child push back.

2. **tongue tip press: down**
   Push down on the child's tongue tip. Repeat and have the child push up.

17

3. **tongue tip press: lateral**
   Push into each side of the child's tongue. Repeat and have the child push back.

4. **tongue tip elevation**
   Place a small dental floss holder with floss in it behind the child's front teeth. Have the child tap or sustain touch on the floss with her tongue tip.

Tongue Back Elevation Techniques

These techniques are important for /k, g, er, r/ and /y/ sounds.

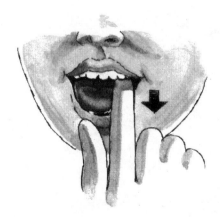

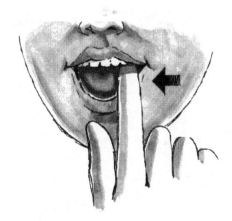

1. **tongue back press: top**
   Push down on the top back of each side of the child's tongue.

2. **tongue back press: sides**
   Push into the back sides of the child's tongue.

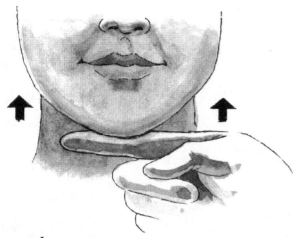

3. **tongue base press**
   Push up on the base of the child's
   tongue with your index finger.

Tongue Lateral Margin Elevation and Spreading Techniques

These techniques are important for /t, d, n, s, z, sh, ch, j, er, r, l/ and /y/ sounds.

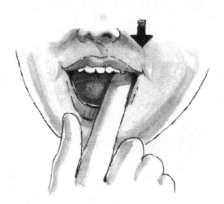

1. **tongue side press: in**
   Push along each side of the
   child's tongue.

2. **tongue side press: down**
   Push down on each side of the child's
   child's tongue.

19

3. **tongue spread**
   Place a standard-size dental floss holder
   between the child's molars. Have the child
   spread his tongue so its sides touch the sides
   of the dental floss holder.

Tongue Retraction Techniques

These techniques are important for /k, g, y/ and /r/ sounds. You can also use the tongue tapping
technique from the *Central Groove of the Tongue Techniques* on page 17 using deep pressure.

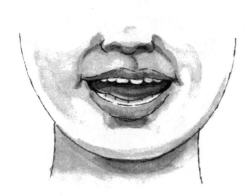

1. **tongue bite**
   Have the child gently bite on the sides
   of her tongue between her molars and
   slide her tongue back.

2. **tongue stroke**
   Stroke the child's tongue along the
   central groove from halfway back
   to the tongue tip.

20

Facial Muscles

These facial muscles are some of the important ones for speech production.

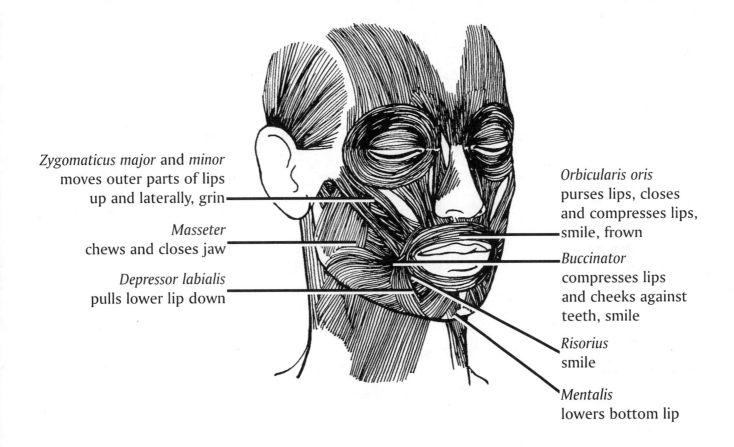

Zygomaticus major and *minor*
moves outer parts of lips
up and laterally, grin

Masseter
chews and closes jaw

Depressor labialis
pulls lower lip down

Orbicularis oris
purses lips, closes
and compresses lips,
smile, frown

Buccinator
compresses lips
and cheeks against
teeth, smile

Risorius
smile

Mentalis
lowers bottom lip

Oral-Motor Equipment

Gather all suggested materials to make an oral-motor therapy equipment box. We suggest a light-weight box with a hinged lid and compartments.

Some materials may be found at the grocery store, at medical supply stores, through Mealtimes (New Visions), or the M.O.R.E program. (See reference list.)

Materials

- alcohol
- antibacterial soap
- aquarium tubing (clear plastic tubing of different diameters, available at pet stores)
- blowing toys (See pages 31-32 for examples.)
- blunt flat toothpicks
- coffee stirrers
- cotton swabs
- dental floss
- Y-shaped dental floss holders, standard size
- edible treats**
- Infa-dents®
- lipstick
- mirror
- mouthwash
- protective gloves
- regular and Nuk® toothbrushes
- straws of various sizes and shapes (cocktail, wide, narrow, straight, curly)
- tongue depressors
- Toothettes®
- washcloth
- Wet Ones®

**Edible treats include crackers, raisins, Hot Tamales® candy, War Heads® candy, peanut butter, chewing gum, marshmallow cream, jelly, Fruit Roll-Ups®, String Thing®, caramel suckers, red licorice braids, Sour Patch Kids® candy, pepperoni slices, dill pickles, and pretzels.*

Classroom Program

Easy Does It For Articulation: An Oral-Motor Approach can be adapted for use with a whole classroom to promote speech development, sound awareness, auditory processing, and early literacy skills. Begin with **Chapter 1: Bilabial Sounds** and progress through each chapter in succession. They are arranged by the placement features of the sounds. See each chapter for specific techniques.

A reproducible *Classroom Lesson Plan* is provided on page 24 and sample lesson plans are provided on pages 25 and 26. Each 15-20 minute session should begin with a brief whole body wake-up. For younger children, do a fun activity such as hopping like a bunny for bilabial productions or pretend to be a galloping horse while clicking the tongue for lingua-alveolar /t, d/. For older children, do general exercises such as stretches, jumping rope, sit-ups, or running. Dancing is a great way to wake up the whole body for all age groups. Follow this with a slow or quiet movement such as being a leaf slowly falling to the ground. This will help the children modulate their activity level and attention.

Then, have the children sit in a circle facing you and do face wake-up activities such as face pats on themselves and jaw stability techniques like pressing in on the points of their chins. Follow this with vocal warm-ups such as imitation of vowels, vowel sequences, and funny sounds. Suggested activities under each chapter can be used to facilitate target sound productions.

After vocal warm-ups, give the children a quick food treat. See the **Taste and Food Activities** section in each chapter for ideas. As they complete the food treat, introduce the sound you'll be targeting for the week. Show an alphabet letter to represent the sound to increase early literacy and sound-symbol awareness. Say the speech sound and talk about how it is made, where the articulators are placed, how the air stream is shaped, and if the sound is long or short, voiced or unvoiced.

Explain to the children that they will be doing mouth exercises to help them make this sound in isolation and in words. Demonstrate a direct facilitation technique and have the children imitate it by doing it on themselves. Help the children who have difficulty. Continue with several other facilitation techniques. Always name the articulator or its parts that are touched. Say the isolated speech sound and have the children imitate it three or more times.

Hold up word pictures from the chapter containing the target sound or use written words with the target sound underlined. Have the children imitate several words while listening for the target sound. You can use the hand signals in the *Materials Book* to further cue the sound. Pictures with the sound in other positions of words may also be used. Copy the pictures used for follow up in the classroom. Give the teacher a copy of the lesson plan and ask if she can incorporate a brief oral-motor stimulation time followed by production of target words several times during the week, or at the very least, review production of the practice words with her class.

End each session with an isometric exercise such as having the children push against a wall with their hands, push their hands together for a few seconds, or give themselves big squeezing hugs. This helps modulate the children's arousal states and enables them to be more focused, calm, and attentive.

Classroom Lesson Plan

Sound Group _____

Implementor(s) _____

Date(s) _____

Whole Body Activities	Face Wake-Ups/Jaw Stability	Direct Techniques	Speech Practice
			1. Vocal warm-up
			2. Target sound production in isolation/syllables _____
			3. Imitate or label pictures with target sound

Taste and Food Activities

Easy Does It for Articulation

Sample Classroom Lesson Plan

Sound Group __p b m__

Implementor(s) _____

Date(s) _____

Whole Body Activities	Face Wake-Ups/Jaw Stability	Direct Techniques	Speech Practice
1. Bunny Hop or 2. Tug of War	1. Face Pats 2. Lip Smacking 3. Push in on chin with thumb for jaw stability	1. Use index finger to rub around lips or 2. Have children smile, then purse lips. Repeat sequence 3 times. or 3. Blow cotton balls by blowing through a straw.	1. Vocal warm-up a. produce isolated long vowel sounds b. hum a well-known tune 2. Target sound production in isolation/syllables __b__ a. isolation b. CV syllables 3. Imitate or abel pictures with target sound _initial /b/ words_ boy boat beam bus build back

Taste and Food Activities

1. Have children suck on small Popsicles.
2. Give children a chewy food. Have children chew food, keeping lips closed. Remind children to smack lips between bites.

Easy Does It for Articulation

Sample Classroom Lesson Plan

Sound Group _t, d, n_

Whole Body Activities	Face Wake-Ups/Jaw Stability	Direct Techniques	Speech Practice
Row Your Boat: Have children separate into pairs, putting hands and feet together as they sit on floor. Have them rock back and forth, holding hands to make a boat.	1. Face pats 2. Have the children clean teeth with tongue, licking upper teeth from molar to molar between the gum and lip. 3. Have child open mouth against resistance for jaw stability.	1. Have the child rub the sides and tip of tongue and inside of alveolar ridge with index finger. *or* 2. Give each child a straw or coffee stirrer and have the child hold it laterally behind his top front teeth with his tongue for count of 10.	1. Vocal warm-up a. produce long sustained vowels in isolation b. produce vowel sequences 2. Target sound production in isolation/syllables _d_ a. isolation b. CV syllables 3. Imitate or label pictures with target sound *initial /d/ words* day done down deep door dish

Taste and Food Activities

1. Have the child hold a long, chewy food against alveolar ridge with the front of his tongue.
or
2. Put a sticky food on the child's upper lip and have him lick it off.

Using The Tracking Sheets

The *Tracking Sheet for Oral-Motor Stimulation* and the *Tracking Sheet for Speech Practice* will help you plan and record therapy objectives and progress. The *Tracking Sheet for Speech Practice* is on page 28 and is to be duplicated as needed. A *Tracking Sheet for Oral-Motor Stimulation* is found at the end of each chapter.

How to use the *Tracking Sheet for Oral-Motor Stimulation*:

1. Select and copy the tracking sheet for the target sound group or phoneme. Put the date in the appropriate column. Mark activities as completed in this column.

2. Explain to the child what you will be working on, including the sequence you'll follow and the target speech sound.

3. Select a whole body activity. After it's completed, write a plus (+) for active participation or a minus (-) for refusal/difficulty with participation in the column next to the activity. Do this for all activities attempted. Not all activities need to be attempted. Note comments about successes, failures, or concerns in the Comments section.

4. Move through the face wake-ups, jaw stability, vocal warm-ups, and taste and food activities sections. Mark each activity attempted with a plus or minus. Enter comments as appropriate, particularly the reason for a minus mark (i.e., refusal, tactile defensiveness, rejection, fearful, etc.).

5. Once warm-ups are completed, proceed to the direct facilitation techniques. Select a technique that addresses the child's specific needs. Implement it three times, then mark the tracking sheet with a plus or minus. Enter comments as to the effect, the child's response, etc. Select another technique and do the same. Do for each technique implemented.

6. List other techniques/cues used and mark them with a plus or minus.

7. As the direct facilitation techniques are completed and speech tasks are introduced, use the *Tracking Sheet for Speech Practice*.

How to use the *Tracking Sheet for Speech Practice*:

1. Make a copy of the tracking sheet.

2. Write in the date and target sound(s).

3. Select the objective column and write in the percentage of correct responses and important comments. Specific syllables and words targeted can be noted.

4. Follow this procedure for all speech targets. Several different sounds may be tracked at one time using this sheet.

Tracking Sheet for Speech Practice

Child's Name _____

Therapist _____

Date	Target Sound	Establishing Placement	Practice in Isolation	Practice in Syllables	Initial Word Practice	Final Word Practice	Medial Word Practice	Multisyllabic Word Practice	Phrases & Sentences	Comments

Answers to Common Questions

Why should I use this approach?

"... a mild problem with oral-motor control can make intelligible speech difficult"

Suzanne Evans Morris

Some children require more direct intervention to develop the sensory awareness and motor strength, precision, and coordination for adequate speech production. Some need to develop a motor memory for speech sounds. This approach teaches the skills needed for successful speech production.

What information do I need about the child before I begin the program?

Evaluation information including medical and developmental history, speech development, oral-motor skills, oral mechanism exam, body tone, oral sensitivity, hearing status, and food allergies.

What cautions should I be aware of?

See **Program Guidelines** on page 10.

What do I tell parents about oral-motor techniques?

Oral-motor facilitation is a more direct way to teach new speech skills. Using this approach will help the child improve his speech by providing more cues and facilitation than auditory and visual cues alone. Share the **Program Sequence** information on pages 7-9 with parents to give them a better understanding of the program you will be implementing.

What equipment do I need?

See the list on page 22.

What can I use for a bite block?

If you don't have a commercial bite block, you can use any of the following: a cocktail straw, dental floss holder, coffee stirrer, tongue depressor, gum, licorice twist, pretzel, carrot stick, or a sucker stick.

How do I choose first targets?

Probe. Look at developmental sequences, easiest oral-motor movements, stimulability, and sounds that will most improve intelligibility.

How many times do I repeat a facilitation technique?

Generally three times in a row during the therapy session.

Do I use deep or light pressure when applying oral facilitation techniques?

Deep pressure is a firm stroke used to desensitize and facilitate. Light pressure is a soft rub that increases awareness. Generally, use deep pressure. Some children, however, respond best to light input. You'll need to determine which type of touch works best for individual children.

What do I do if the child refuses oral-motor stimulation?

See **Program Guidelines** on page 10 about tactile defensiveness and resistance to oral-motor tasks. It also helps to make the activities fun.

Doesn't this take a long time each session?

At first, yes, but it is time well spent. It's effective because it gives a direct way to get sound productions where other types of stimulation failed and it may facilitate more than one speech sound at a time. Some children require more direct facilitation than others. You will reduce the amount of time spent doing oral-motor activities as the child begins to successfully make target sounds without the direct intervention.

When do I move on? or *How long do I implement the oral-motor facilitation techniques?*

Once the child can consistently produce the speech sound and stabilize it at the word level, you don't need to continue the stimulation. You may need to review the facilitation techniques when introducing the sound in other positions in words. Attention to body and jaw positioning and stability, however, remain important.

What other techniques can I use?

Temperature variations of materials can provide extra sensory input, as can variations in textures. Cold, rough, and uneven textures are more alerting and noticeable to the child. Intensifying tastes such as using purer concentrations, and smelling the taste first can provide increased sensory input.

What are some sucking activities? Why are they used?

Sucking increases lip closure, lip strength, gradated jaw closure and stability, and the use of the cheek muscles. It improves inspiration, postural stability, and trunk-head-neck alignment. It facilitates speech sounds at the back of the mouth such as /k, g, ng, er, r/ and lip sounds such as /p, b, m, w/. Sucking is more beneficial when the straw or tubing is held by the lips, not the teeth.

1. You can change the strength of the suck by using straws of varying widths or by using curly straws. For greater sucking strength, use thicker drinking substances (apple juice mixed with applesauce, milk shakes, semi-melted ice cream, slushes or partially frozen lemonade, or pudding).

2. For older children, mark a line on a clear straw. Have the child suck a colored liquid such as Kool-Aid® up to that point on the straw and hold it.

3. Have the child suck on firm Jell-O® cubes, fruit wedges, or Popsicles.

4. Have the child use a straw to suck items larger than the straw onto the straw opening, and then hold them there briefly. Items to suck could include paper balls, pom-poms, cotton balls, or large beans. Make sure the items are too large to go through the straw. Make a game by picking up the objects and putting them in a container using the straw.

5. Twist and loop a piece of clear aquarium tubing into a design. Have the child use it like a straw.

6. Use citrus or sour flavors such as lemonade, limeade, or cranberry drinks.

What are some blowing activities? Why are they used?

Blowing is excellent for facilitating lip closure, respiration and breath support for speech, and jaw stability and grading. It helps develop the muscles of the tongue, cheek, jaw, and lips, as well as organizing the sensorimotor system. It facilitates speech sounds that require graded air flow, lip rounding, and lip closure. Patty Oetter's M.O.R.E. program provides more information about blowing. (See reference list.) Make sure the item used for blowing is being held by the lips and not the teeth. Have the child use sustained breaths during blowing.

1. Have the child blow sound makers, paper horns that roll up, party favors, and pinwheels.

2. Have the child blow bubbles using wands, bubble pipes, straws, or flexible tubing (aquarium tubing).

3. Play with blowing toys that have moving parts or that make interesting sounds when blown.

4. Have the child blow cotton balls, paper wads, feathers, small balls, or lightweight figures. Put them on a table and have blowing races or see who can blow them off the table. You can use a straw for this too.

5. Make bubble "soup." Put a small amount of dishwashing detergent in a pan with a few inches of water. Put one end of a piece of aquarium tubing into the pan. Have the child blow through the tubing into the pan to make lots of bubbles. Use caution with young children who may suck rather than blow.

6. Have the child hum to music, blow a harmonica or other wind instrument, whistle, or blow into a soda pop bottle to make it whistle.

7. Do the story of *The Three Little Pigs*. You and the child can "huff and puff" and blow a paper house down.

8. Put drops of watercolor or tempera paint onto a sheet of paper. Have the child blow on the paint through a straw to create designs.

9. Use a blown-up balloon or bubbles and have the child keep them in the air by blowing them.

The child still can't say the sound. Now what do I do?

Ask yourself the following questions if the child persists in having difficulty achieving and stabilizing articulator or sound placement:

◆ Are the child's body and head in the correct position?

◆ Did you precede oral stimulation with a whole body and face wake-up to fire up the speech mechanism?

◆ Is the jaw placed in a neutral position and is it stable? Did you try using a bite block?

◆ Does the oral area need to be desensitized?

◆ Does the child have normal muscle tone, high tone, low tone, or mixed tone, particularly in the face and oral area? Has this been addressed?

◆ Are you doing the technique correctly?

◆ Did you try other techniques?

◆ Did you quit too soon? Could the child be successful if you continued to apply the technique for additional sessions?

◆ Did you implement troubleshooting suggestions?

◆ Did you consult with a pediatric OT or PT?

◆ Is the child ready for this goal, or should you work on another speech placement and sound, and come back to this one later?

◆ Is there anything else impeding progress such as a short lingual frenulum, hearing loss, allergies, or enlarged tonsils and adenoids?

◆ Does the child have other developmental delays? If so, his progress may be slower.

Who should I ask if I have questions?

A SLP, OT, or PT trained in pediatric oral-motor techniques.

Chapter 1
Bilabial Sounds /p, b, m, w/

How /p/ and /b/ sounds are made:
The lips are closed briefly to impound and build up air pressure and then the lips are opened and the air is released in an explosion. The vocal folds vibrate for the /b/.

How the /m/ sound is made:
The lips are together and a continuous nasalized sound is resonated as it passes through the oropharynx, nasopharynx, and nose. The vocal folds vibrate.

How the /w/ sound is made:
Vibrated air passes through the lips which are rounded and slightly protruded. The teeth are slightly open and the back of the tongue is slightly elevated.

Preparing for Speech

After you prepare the child's body, face, and speech mechanism for speech practice, provide direct techniques for sound facilitation. Follow this with speech practice. Implement troubleshooting techniques as needed. Don't forget to wear protective gloves when working in or around a child's face and mouth.

Whole Body Wake-Ups

Have the child:

- do short burst of movement activities such as jumping, punching, skipping, bouncing, or kicking for /p/, /b/, or /w.

- do long, sustained movements with extension or flexion such as sliding, swinging, rolling, or pulling for /m/.

- do resistive movements such as pulling hard on a rope or carrying a heavy chair.

- sustain blowing or do resistive sucking through a straw. (See pages 30-32 for suggestions.)

- do the Bunny Hop around the room.

Face Wake-Ups

1. Have the child pat his cheeks, lips, and under his chin using his index and middle fingers.

2. Wipe or stroke the child's face with texture, such as a washcloth. Begin at the point of origin of each facial muscle and stroke to the point of muscle insertion at the lips. Stroke around the lips in a circular motion. (See page 21 for an illustration of the facial muscles.)

3. Have the child smack his lips several times and then throw kisses with an exaggerated pucker.

4. Have the child puff out his cheeks and not let the air escape for a few seconds (i.e., maintain a lip seal).

Jaw Stability

Gently push downward on the child's chin as he attempts to keep his mouth closed. Then, push upward while the child attempts to open his mouth (resistance).

Provide proprioceptive input by pushing inward on the point of the chin with deep pressure for a few seconds and/or massaging the muscles around the temporal-mandibular joint.

Vocal Warm-Ups

Have the child:

- ◆ imitate isolated vowels and vowel sequences.

- ◆ imitate funny sounds such as raspberries, motorboat sounds, and lip trilling during vocalization.

- ◆ hum or blow a kazoo.

Taste and Food Activities to Facilitate Lip Closure

1. Give the child a piece of a food or have him chew up a food with a sour or tingly taste to wake up the mouth like lemon, sour candy, or hot candy like Hot Tamales or War Heads.

2. Have the child briefly suck on a Popsicle or an ice cube.

3. Put one end of a long food like cooked spaghetti, Fruit Roll-Up cut into strips, or String Thing candy between the child's lips. The child must get all of it in his mouth only using his lips and tongue — no hands allowed!

4. Have the child chew food with her lips closed. Let her smack her lips in between bites.

5. To facilitate jaw grading, have the child bite crackers or celery and carrot sticks.

Direct Techniques to Facilitate Sound Placement

Repeat each technique three times. Review the *Program Sequence, Program Guidelines,* and *Illustrated Oral-Motor Techniques* in the introductory pages as needed. For /p, b, m/, implement direct techniques 1 through 9. For /w/, implement direct techniques 1, 3, 4, 5, and 10.

1. Do "bunny noses." Place your index finger and middle finger on either side of the child's nose. Vibrate your fingers as you move them down to the child's upper lip. Hold them there briefly, then release.

2. Place your index finger flat above the child's upper lip. Apply pressure by pushing into the area. Hold for a few seconds and release.

3. Put your index finger and middle finger into a V shape. Use this V to press up and out at the upper boundary of the child's upper lip. Then, use the V to press down and out at the lower boundary of the child's lower lip. Hold each briefly.

4. Put your index finger and thumb at the midline of the child's upper lip. Stretch the lip from the midline to the corner by spreading your finger and thumb. Hold briefly and release. Repeat for the lower lip.

5. Repeat #4 but have the child try to pucker his lips.

6. Have the child close his lips tightly and keep them closed as you attempt to gently pull them open (resistance). Do this at the midline of the lips.

7. Put a washcloth, straw, or a tongue depressor flat between the child's lips. See if he can hold on to the item as you gently attempt to pull it out. Make sure the object is between his lips only, not his teeth.

8. Pull forward on the child's upper lip, holding at the midline, right above the lip. Have the child retract his lips to say the vowel /i/ as you hold his lip, providing resistance.

9. To increase sensory awareness of lip contact for /p, b, m/, rub the contact surfaces of the child's upper and lower lips with texture like a washcloth or toothbrush, or rub mouthwash on each lip with a cotton swab.

10. To facilitate lip rounding for /w/, have the child do blowing activities using large straws or plastic aquarium tubing.

Tips and Troubleshooting Techniques

For the child who has difficulty achieving or maintaining lip closure or lip rounding:

1. Make the child aware of the physical characteristics of the sound, whether it's a short popping sound or a long sustained sound. Use a verbal description or body movements.

2. Use touch cues to the child's face as he produces the target bilabial sound in isolation, syllables, or words. Tap the child's closed lips with two fingers using light pressure for the /p/. Do the same for /b/, but use a deeper pressure. Touch the child's lips for /m/ using sustained pressure. Circle the child's lips with your fingers for /w/. Use hand signals to cue the child to use appropriate lip placement for these sounds. (See pages 174-176 in the *Materials Book.*)

3. Check the positioning of the child's body. If the child's head is tilted back and his trunk is bent, it will encourage a mouth-open position with relatively flaccid lips. Make sure the child is in 90°-90°-90° positioning with his head at midline and his chin slightly tucked.

4. Watch the child to monitor for a pattern of mouth breathing. Check the status of the tonsils. Enlarged tonsils and adenoids may encourage the child to breathe with his mouth open. Consult with an ENT on the status of the upper respiratory system to see if there is a reason for the mouth breathing.

5. Watch how the child eats to see if he uses a closed-mouth or a wide-open mouth chew. Facilitate chewing with the lips closed during eating as needed.

6. Check for jaw stability. If jaw stability is a problem during speech practice, have the child cup his jaw in his hands, or have him place his elbow on a table with his chin resting in his hand.

7. If the child keeps his tongue forward and protruded at rest, you may need to work on tongue retraction along with the lip closure techniques. For example, tap the central groove of the tongue from the front to the center of the tongue.

8. If the child has too much tension in his lips, hold his upper lip and gently shake it. If he is closing rather than rounding his lips for /w/, use your thumb and index finger to stroke each lip from the center to each corner, then gently shake it.

9. Go from another sound production to the bilabials.

    ◆ Have the child hum, then manually open his jaw to produce a /b/.

    ◆ Have the child say /h/ as you manually compress and release his lips for /p/.

    ◆ Have the child say /ah/ as you manually compress his jaw and lower lip to contact the upper lip for /m/ or /b/.

◆ Have the child go from /oo/ to /w/. You could also have the child go from an elongated /oo/ with exaggerated lip rounding to another long vowel. You'll get /w/ between the vowels (i.e., from long /o/ to long /e/, you'll get "owee").

10. Have the child feel the air burst for /p/ and /b/ with his hand or hold a paper strip or feather in front of his lips as he says the sound. Have him place a finger along his nose to feel the vibration as he says /m/.

11. Put on lipstick and make lip prints on a sheet of paper during sound production to check lip placement.

12. If there is not enough lip rounding for /w/, increase lip tension by:

◆ having the child do blowing activities or resistive sucking.

◆ providing manual vibration to the child's facial muscles, particularly around the lips.

◆ stretching the child's upper and lower lips, starting at the midline and going to the corners using deep pressure. Hold briefly and release.

◆ having the child say "eee" or smile while you gently try to push his lips into a pucker (resistance).

◆ having the child hold a pucker while you gently try to pull his lips into a smile (resistance).

◆ having the child put his index finger in front of his lips while saying "sh." This "be quiet" cue can pull the child's lips forward and round them.

Tracking Sheet for Oral-Motor Stimulation

Name _____

Preparing for Speech for the /p, b, m, w/ sounds	Dates			
1. Whole Body Wake-Ups				
a. burst of movement				
b. sustained movements				
c. sustained blowing/resistive sucking				
d. "Bunny Hop"				
2. Face Wake-Ups				
a. pats parts of face				
b. stroke facial muscles				
c. lip smacking and throwing kisses				
d. puff cheeks				
3. Jaw Stability				
a. open/close mouth against resistance				
b. push in on chin				
c. rest chin in hands				
4. Vocal Warm-Ups				
a. isolated vowel productions				
b. vowel sequences				
c. funny sounds: motor boat, raspberry, lip trilling				
d. humming, kazoo				
5. Taste and Food Activities				
a. _____				
b. _____				
c. _____				
6. Direct Facilitation Techniques				
a. bunny noses				
b. sustained pressure above upper lip				
c. V-pressure above and below lips				
d. lip stretching				
e. resistive tasks (stretch with pucker, pull lips open, pull out object, retract lips)				
f. rubbing lips				
g. blowing				
h. other techniques/cues				
_____				
_____				
_____				

Comments:

Activities

Give the child the worksheet and materials necessary to complete each activity. Practice each target sound, syllable, or word three times. Write target syllables or words on the worksheets or glue on word pictures. Provide all the cues the child needs to successfully produce the target sound. Send completed worksheets home for additional practice.

Materials needed for the /p, b, m, w/ worksheets:

- markers
- crayons
- scissors
- glue
- pencil
- sheet of paper
- construction paper
- watercolors or paints

Activities for the /p/ sound

1. On the *Purple Peanut Eater* worksheet, have the child say a /p/ sound three times in isolation and then connect one or two dots.

2. Write /p/ + vowel or vowel + /p/ syllable combinations on each bird on the *Perky Peepers* worksheet. Have the child say a syllable three times and then color a bird.

3. On the *Paint by Number* worksheet, have the child say an initial /p/ word three times and then color or paint an object in the picture.

4. Write final /p/ words on the lines by the mountain on the *At the End of Your Rope* worksheet. Have the child say one of the words three times and then color a flower on his way up the mountain.

5. On the *Open Says Me!* worksheet, cut along the dotted lines around the doors. Write some medial /p/ words on a sheet of paper and glue it behind the doors. Have the child open the doors so he can see his words as he practices them. Then, encourage the child to add more medial /p/ words and to decorate the chest.

6. Write five multisyllabic /p/ words on the clown's sign on the *Puppet Show* worksheet. Have the child practice each word three times and then draw his own puppet on the stage.

7. On the *Slumber Party* worksheet, there are many /p/, /b/, /m/, and /w/ words pictured in all positions of words for additional practice or for phrase and sentence practice. After the child has identified and practiced the /p/ words, have him circle the pictures that have his target sound.

   The following /p/ words are targeted in this scene:

pajamas	pillow	puppy	lamp
paper	pinwheel	purse	sleeping bag
pie	ponytail	backpack	
piece	popcorn	cup	

Activities for the /b/ sound

1. On the *Bouncing Bertha* worksheet, have the child say a /b/ sound in isolation three times and then color a ball.

2. Write /b/ + vowel or vowel + /b/ syllable combinations on the toys on the *Grab a Toy* worksheet. Have the child say a syllable three times and then color a toy.

3. Write initial /b/ words on the buttons at the bottom of the *Button Up* worksheet. Have the child say the word on one of the buttons three times and then cut it out and glue it to the sweater.

4. Write final /b/ words on the food at the bottom of the *Build a Sub* worksheet. Have the child say a word on one of the food items three times before he colors the food for his sub sandwich. Then, have the child cut out and glue the foods onto his sub bun to make a sandwich.

5. Write medial /b/ words on the robot on the *Robbie Robot* worksheet. Have the child say a word on Robbie three times and then color part of the robot.

6. Write multisyllabic /b/ words on the spiders on the *Spider's Web* worksheet. Have the child say a word on a spider three times and then draw a line from the spider to the web.

7. On the *Slumber Party* worksheet, there are many /p/, /b/, /m/, and /w/ words pictured in all positions of words for additional practice or for phrase and sentence practice. After the child has identified and practiced the /b/ words, have him circle the pictures that have his target sound.

   The following /b/ words are targeted in this scene:

backpack	bottoms	sleeping bag
bed	bowl	table
bedroom	box	wastebasket
bedspread	button	

Activities for the /m/ sound

1. On the *Mowing Mickey* worksheet, have the child say an /m/ sound in isolation and then color a section of grass.

2. Write /m/ + vowel or vowel + /m/ syllable combinations in the large spots on the cows on the *Merry Milk Cows* worksheet. Have the child say a syllable on a spot three times and then color the spot.

3. Write initial /m/ words in the monster's footprints on the *Monster Mess* worksheet. Have the child say a word on a footprint three times and then color the footprint.

4. Write final /m/ words on the tree branches on the *Out on a Limb* worksheet. Have the child say a word on a tree branch three times and then draw a plum in the basket.

5. Write medial /m/ words on the rubber ducks on the *Summer Time* worksheet. Have the child say a word on a duck three times and then color the duck.

6. Write multisyllabic /m/ words on the *Marshmallow Roast* worksheet. Have the child say a word three times and then color a marshmallow.

7. On the *Slumber Party* worksheet, there are many /p/, /b/, /m/, and /w/ words pictured in all positions of words for additional practice or for phrase and sentence practice. After the child has identified and practiced the /m/ words, have him circle the pictures that have his target sound.

   The following /m/ words are targeted in this scene:

mess	home
money	pajamas
mouth	room
empty	watermelon

Activities for the /w/ sound

1. On the *Blown Away* worksheet, have the child say a /w/ sound in isolation three times and then color a boat.

2. Write /w/ + vowel or vowel + /w/ syllable combinations on the *Windmill* worksheet. Have the child say a syllable three times and then color a blade on the windmill.

3. Cut out the towels on the bottom of the *Wet Mutts* worksheet and write initial /w/ words on them. Have the child say a word on a towel three times and then glue the towel on a puppy.

4. Write medial /w/ words on the *End Over End* worksheet. Have the child say a word three times and then draw a line from one X to another. When all of the lines have been drawn, let the child color the girl's leotard.

5. Cut stars out of yellow construction paper and write multisyllabic /w/ words on them. Have the child say a word on a star three times and then glue it on the *Somewhere Out There* worksheet.

6. On the *Slumber Party* worksheet, there are many /p/, /b/, /m/ and /w/ words pictured in initial and medial positions of words for additional practice or for phrase and sentence practice. After the child has identified and practiced the /w/ words, have him circle the pictures that have his target sound.

Bilabial Sounds
Easy Does It for Articulation   41

The following /w/ words are targeted in this scene:

wallet	whisper	cartwheel
wastebasket	wig	pinwheel
watermelon	window	sandwich

Chapter 2

Labiodental Sounds /f, v/

> **How /f/ and /v/ sounds are made:**
> The lower lip moves upward to lightly contact the lower edge of the upper front teeth.
> A continuous airstream flows through this contact to produce a friction noise. The vocal
> folds are vibrating for the /v/.

Preparing for Speech

After you prepare the child's body, face, and speech mechanism for speech practice, provide direct techniques for sound facilitation. Follow this with speech practice. Implement troubleshooting techniques as needed. Don't forget to wear protective gloves when working in or around a child's face and mouth.

Whole Body Wake-Ups

Have the child:

◆ do long, sustained movements such as sliding, swinging, rolling, skating, or squeezing something like a balloon filled with flour, an empty two-liter bottle with the top on, or a Nerf® ball.

◆ sustain blowing. (See pages 31-32 for suggested activities.)

◆ blow with different-sized straws or aquarium tubing, or blow into a 2-liter bottle with her lips around the top to encourage graded jaw movements. (ability to control the amount of jaw opening)

◆ chew on chewy candy or foods like raisins or chewing gum for graded jaw movements.

◆ work on breath support for speech by bouncing on a Hippity-Hop® or large therapy ball, swinging on her tummy on a playground swing, doing crunch type sit-ups, or jumping up and down.

Face Wake-Ups

1. Have the child pat her cheeks, lips, and under the chin using her index and middle fingers.

2. Rub the child's lower lip with your finger or with texture like a towel, Toothette, Infa-dent, or toothbrush. Then, have the child do this to herself.

3. Have the child lick her lower lip and then suck it in between her teeth. Next have the child bite her lower lip or scrape it with her top teeth.

Jaw Stability

Gently push downward on the child's chin as she attempts to keep her mouth closed. Then, push upward while the child attempts to open her mouth.

Provide proprioceptive input by pushing inward on the point of the chin with deep pressure for a few seconds and/or massaging the muscles around the temporal-mandibular joint.

Vocal Warm-Ups

Have the child:

- ◆ imitate isolated vowels and vowel sequences.

- ◆ imitate /h/ and /ah/ in long sustained productions.

- ◆ imitate a long sigh.

- ◆ imitate sounds such as an airplane engine sound, lip trilling, or whispering.

Taste and Food Activities to Facilitate "Teeth-on-Lip" Contact

1. Put peanut butter or other sticky food on the child's lower lip and have her scrape it off using her upper teeth.

2. Have the child briefly suck an ice cube or Popsicle. Rub the ice on her lower lip and on the edge of her upper teeth.

3. Have the child use her front teeth to bite through crackers or carrot and celery sticks to encourage appropriate jaw function.

4. Have the child hold a piece of red licorice or String Thing between her upper teeth and lower lip. Have her pull on the candy using her upper teeth and lower lip as you pull on the other end. Then, have her bite off a piece and chew it up with her lips closed.

Direct Techniques to Facilitate Sound Placement

Repeat each technique three times. Remember that only the lower lip should make contact on labiodental sounds. Review the *Program Sequence*, *Program Guidelines*, and *Illustrated Oral-Motor Techniques* in the introductory pages as needed.

1. Using your index and middle fingers, tap the child's lower lip four or five times gently, but firmly. Do the same on the bottom edge of the child's upper central incisors.

2. Put your index and middle fingers, or your finger and thumb at the midline of the child's lower lip. Stretch the lip as you glide your fingers from the center to the corners. Hold briefly and release.

3. Gently "scratch" the child's lower lip with your fingernail. Dip a cotton swab into mouthwash and rub it on the child's lower lip.

4. Place your index finger along the child's entire lower lip. Apply deep pressure into the lip and hold for four to five seconds.

5. Place your thumb under the child's chin, your index finger on the child's cheek, and your middle finger under the child's lip. With the child's teeth open slightly, gently press upward with your middle finger as you push the child's lip into her mouth between her teeth. (You may also use your thumb on the child's cheek, your index finger under the child's lip, and your middle finger under the child's chin.)

6. Use your fingers to apply sustained pressure to the child's upper teeth to increase awareness.

Tips and Troubleshooting Techniques

For the child who has difficulty achieving or maintaining a labiodental placement:

1. Make the child aware of the physical characteristics of the sound. Use a verbal description or body movements.

2. Use a touch cue, such as tapping the child's lower lip, as she produces the target sound in isolation, syllables, or words. Use hand signals to cue the child to use the teeth-on-lip placement for these sounds. (See pages 174-176 in the *Materials Book*)

3. Check the positioning of the child's body. A bent trunk with the head tilted can encourage a mouth-open position with relatively flaccid lips and impaired respiration for speech.

4. Watch the child for a pattern of mouth-breathing. Check the status of the tonsils. Enlarged tonsils and adenoids may encourage the child to keep her mouth open for breathing purposes. Consult with an ENT on the status of the upper respiratory system to see if there is a reason for mouth breathing.

5. Watch how the child eats to see if she bites with jaw gradation and chews with a mature rotary chew with her lips closed. Facilitate jaw function, rotary chew, and lip closure as needed.

6. Check for jaw stability. If jaw stability is a problem during speech practice, have the child cup her jaw in her hands or have her place her elbow on a table with her chin resting in her hand.

7. If the child has too much tension in her lips so her lips are contacting each other or are retracted:

    ◆ hold the upper lip and gently shake it

    ◆ massage the chin toward the midline, then gently shake the lower lip

    ◆ put your index finger on one corner of the child's lips and your thumb on the other corner of her lips and stroke toward the center

8. If the lower lip is too relaxed, lay your index finger along the child's lower lip and press it down toward her chin as she resists. Then, stroke from the center of the child's lip to the corners by putting your index finger and thumb at the center of her lips and moving them outward, away from each other.

9. If the child is having difficulty getting her jaw and lower lip in the right position, go from another sound production to the labiodentals. Have the child say /h/ as you manually close her jaw some and press her lower lip against her upper teeth. For /v/, have the child say "ah" as you close her jaw and press her lower lip against her upper teeth.

10. If the child is substituting /p/ for /f/ or /b/ for /v/, focus on the continuous airflow for /f/ and /v/. Use blowing techniques with a straw between the child's upper teeth and lower lip. Gradually pull out the straw while the child sustains blowing until her teeth are on her lower lip.

11. Rub the child's lower lip. Place a strip of paper between the child's lower lip and upper teeth. See if she can blow air without losing the paper.

12. If the child puts her lower teeth against her top lip during placement attempts, increase awareness of the lower lip. Make sure the jaw is in a neutral position, and not protruded. You can also:

    ◆ apply pressure, tap, or rub her lower lip

    ◆ have the child bite her lower lip

    ◆ use a mirror

47

Tracking Sheet for Oral-Motor Stimulation

Name _____

Preparing for Speech for the /f, v/ sounds	Dates			
1. Whole Body Wake-Ups				
a. sustained movement				
b. sustained blowing				
c. jaw control and jaw grading				
d. breath support				
2. Face Wake-Ups				
a. pats parts of face				
b. rub lower lip with texture				
c. lick, suck, bite, scrape lower lip				
3. Jaw Stability				
a. open/close mouth against resistance				
b. push in on chin				
c. rest chin in hands				
4. Vocal Warm-Ups				
a. isolated vowel productions				
b. vowel sequences				
c. sustained /h/, /ah/, sigh				
d. sounds: airplane, lip trilling, whispering				
5. Taste and Food Activities				
a. _____				
b. _____				
c. _____				
6. Direct Facilitation Techniques				
a. tap on lower lip				
b. apply stretch to lower lip				
c. scratch or rub lower lip				
d. deep pressure to lower lip				
e. tuck in lower lip with jaw support				
f. sustained pressure to upper teeth				
g. other techniques/cues				
_____				
_____				
_____				

Comments:

Activities

Give the child the worksheet and materials necessary to complete each activity. Practice each target sound, syllable, or word three times. Write target syllables or words on the worksheets or glue on word pictures. Provide all the cues the child needs to successfully produce the target sound. Send completed worksheets home for additional practice.

Materials needed for the /f, v/ worksheets

- ◆ markers
- ◆ crayons
- ◆ pencil

Activities for /f/

1. On the *Fan-tastic Feeling* worksheet, have the child say the /f/ sound in isolation and then color a streamer on the fan.

2. Write /f/ + vowel or vowel + /f/ syllable combinations on the *Gopher Get Together* worksheet. Have the child say a syllable three times and then color a gopher.

3. Write initial /f/ words on the fish on the *Friend or Foe?* worksheet. Have the child say a word on a fish three times and then color the fish.

4. Write final /f/ words on the *Tee Off!* worksheet. Have the child say a word on the sheet three times and then draw a golf ball on a tee.

5. Write medial /f/ words on the signs on the *Safety First* worksheet. Have the child say a word on a sign three times and then color the sign.

6. Write multisyllabic /f/ words on the *Perfect Form* worksheet. Have the child trace around a circle with her finger or a pencil as she says each word three times.

7. On the *Flower Shop* worksheet, there are many /f/ and /v/ words pictured in all positions of words for additional practice or for phrase and sentence practice. After the child has identified and practiced the /f/ words, have her circle the pictures that have her target sound.

   The following /f/ words are targeted in this scene:

face	five	a few	leaf
feet	flower	beautiful	refrigerator
fern	flower shop	butterfly	telephone
finger	four	daffodil	

Activities for /v/

1. On the *Over and Over* worksheet, have the child say the /v/ sound in isolation as she traces the plane's loops with her finger or a pencil. Then let the child color one of the airplanes.

2. Write /v/ + vowel or vowel + /v/ syllable combinations on the *Seems Like Spring* worksheet. Have the child say a syllable three times and then put an X on a fly.

3. Write initial /v/ words on the students' shirts on the *My Vote Counts* worksheet. Have the child say a word on a shirt three times and then put a check mark on the tally board.

4. Write final /v/ words on the beehive on the *Coming Home* worksheet. Have the child say a word on the beehive three times and then draw a line from a bee to the beehive.

5. Write medial /v/ words on the suitcases on the *Leaving On Vacation* worksheet. Have the child say a word on a suitcase three times and then color the suitcase.

6. Write multisyllabic /v/ words on the *Pavement Art* worksheet. Have the child say a word on the sidewalk three times and then trace one of the drawings on the sidewalk with a crayon or pencil.

7. On the *Flower Shop* worksheet, there are many /f/ and /v/ words pictured in all positions of words for additional practice or for phrase and sentence practice. After the child has identified and practiced the /v/ words, have her circle the pictures that have her target sound.

   The following /v/ words are targeted in this scene:

vase	dove	seven
vest	gloves	sleeve
violets	ivy	
above	over	

Chapter 3
Lingua-alveolar Sounds /t, d, n/

How /t/, /d/, and /n/ sounds are made:
The tongue tip is pressed against the alveolar ridge behind the upper front teeth while the sides of the tongue are in contact with the sides of the teeth and the gums. Air pressure is built up behind the tongue and then released for /t/ and /d/. Nasalized air is sustained for the /n/. The vocal folds vibrate for the /d/ and /n/.

Preparing for Speech

After you prepare the child's body, face, and speech mechanism for speech practice, provide direct techniques for sound facilitation. Follow this with speech practice. Implement troubleshooting techniques as needed. Don't forget to wear protective gloves when working in or around a child's face and mouth.

Whole Body Wake-Ups

Have the child:

◆ do short burst-of-movement activities such as jumping, punching a bag, skipping, bouncing on a Hippity Hop® ball, or playing Hopscotch for /t/ and /d/.

◆ do sustained resistance activities like pulling or hanging on a rope, pushing a heavy box, carrying a heavy object, pedaling a tricycle or Big Wheel®, or swinging for /n/.

◆ do resistive sucking through a straw. (See pages 30-31 for suggestions.)

◆ do "Row Your Boat" activity with you. Sit on the floor, facing each other. Hold hands and put your feet together to make a boat. Set up a rocking motion by pulling the child so he rocks forward, then having the child pull you so you rock forward.

Face Wake-Ups

1. Have the child pat his cheeks, lips, and under his chin using his index and middle fingers.

2. Use a gloved finger, Infa-dent, Toothette, or washcloth to rub the child's inner maxillary alveolar ridge three times from molar to molar. Rub the child's tongue along the margins from the tip down one side, then from the tip down the other side three times.

3. Have the child use his fingers to tap his top front and tip of his tongue. Then, have him clean his teeth by licking the front of his upper teeth from molar to molar between the lip and gum.

4. Place a cloth, a piece of thick licorice, or a piece of Fruit Roll-Up between the child's front teeth and pull on it as he keeps his teeth closed.

Jaw Stability

Gently push downward on the chin as the child attempts to keep his mouth closed, then push upward while the child attempts to open his mouth (resistance).

Provide proprioceptive input by pushing inward on the point of the chin with deep pressure for a few seconds and/or massaging the muscles around the temporal-mandibular joint.

Vocal Warm-Ups

Have the child:

- ◆ imitate vowels and vowel sequences.

- ◆ "make the horse go" by clicking his tongue several times on his alveolar ridge. Make sure to stabilize the child's jaw so it's not doing the work. The tongue should be moving independently.

- ◆ put his tongue behind his upper front teeth and suck in to make a fricative sound. Then, have him "squirt" the air out between the central incisors.

Taste and Food Activities to Facilitate Tongue Tip Elevation

1. Have the child chew gum to alert the oral cavity. Use gum that has a cinnamon, spearmint, or peppermint taste. Have the child chew and then hold the gum against his alveolar ridge with his tongue tip for a few seconds. Repeat several times.

2. Have the child hold a long food such as String Thing, strip of Fruit Roll-Ups, a red licorice twist, or a pretzel against his alveolar ridge with the front of his tongue.

3. Have the child chew hot or spicy foods that wake up the mouth like Hot Tamales, War Heads, Sour Patch Kids, dill pickles, or pepperoni slices.

4. Put a sticky food such as peanut butter, jelly, or marshmallow cream on the child's upper lip and have the child lick it off.

5. Place a sticky food on the child's alveolar ridge behind his front teeth and have the child lick it off using the tip and front of his tongue.

Direct Techniques to Facilitate Sound Placement

Repeat each technique three times. Review the *Program Sequence*, *Program Guidelines*, and *Illustrated Oral-Motor Techniques* in the introductory pages as needed.

1. Rub the sides and tip of the child's tongue and his alveolar ridge with texture like a washcloth, Toothette, toothbrush, Infa-dent, or cotton swab. Name the points of contact.

2. Use your finger to apply deep pressure to the front of the child's tongue and to his tongue tip in a series of quick taps.

3. Push down on the front of the child's tongue with your finger as the child attempts to push your finger up. Then, push into the child's tongue tip and have the child attempt to push your finger away with his tongue without moving his head.

4. Use your finger to push into the front sides of the child's tongue. Push toward the midline of the tongue as the child pushes against your finger.

5. To get elevation of the tongue sides and tip, stroke the central groove of the child's tongue from the middle to the tip. Do not elicit a gag.

6. Press down on the front top of the child's tongue at the center. Slowly lift your finger and ask the child to follow your finger with his tongue.

7. Hold a sucker, Popsicle, pretzel, carrot stick, celery stick, or tongue depressor vertically in front of the child's mouth. Without moving his head, have him use his tongue to lick from the bottom to the top of the object. Then, pull down on the object as the child licks up on it.

8. Put a thin cocktail straw or coffee stirrer laterally behind the child's front teeth. Have him hold it there for a count of 10 using only the front of his tongue. Don't let him close his jaw to hold the straw. You can also place the straw on the central groove of the tongue and have him hold it against the alveolus.

Tips and Troubleshooting Techniques

For the child who has difficulty achieving or maintaining tongue elevation:

1. Make the child aware of the physical characteristics of each sound (short, popping sound or long, sustained sound). Use a verbal description or body movements.

2. Use a touch cue such as tapping above the upper lip for /t/ and /d/ as the child produces the target sound in isolation, syllables, or words. Use a sustained touch for /n/. Use hand signals to cue the child to use a tongue-up placement for the lingua-alveolar sounds. (See pages 174-176 in the *Materials Book*.)

3. Check the lingual frenum for adequate length for tongue elevation.

4. Make sure the child is using the tip of his tongue and not the tongue blade for contact with the alveolar ridge. Make sure the front of the tongue is elevating and isn't coming forward between the teeth.

5. Concentrate on establishing independent tongue action from the jaw. Use a thin object between the child's molars like a cocktail straw or the flat surface of a tongue depressor as a bite block. Have the child elevate his tongue tip to the alveolar ridge as he maintains his bite on the object. This will encourage separation of tongue and jaw action.

   Provide jaw stability techniques such as having the child rest his chin in his cupped hands or on his fist as he attempts sound productions.

6. Increase awareness of the tongue tip by rubbing it with a cotton swab dipped in mouthwash. Then, touch the cotton swab to the point of contact on the alveolar ridge.

7. Tie a string through a peppermint or spearmint Lifesaver® and put it on the front of the child's tongue. Have him place his tongue tip through the Lifesaver, then lift and hold it on his alveolar ridge for a few seconds. You can also use the end of a bubble wand.

8. Have the child hold a small dental floss holder with floss in it behind his front teeth. Have the child tap the floss or sustain touch on the floss with the tip of his tongue. You can also stretch a piece of dental floss between the canine and cuspid teeth for the same effect.

9. If the child is having trouble producing /t/, /d/, or /n/, begin from another sound production such as going from /s/ to /t/, from /z/ to /d/, or from a sustained vowel to /n/.

10. To get voicing on /d/ and /n/, go from another voiced sound like "ah" ("ah-d" *odd* or "ah-n" *on*).

11. If the child isn't getting enough air build-up for the sounds, or isn't getting a good plosive air release on /t/ or /d/, work on respiration and breath support while he is producing the sound.

    ◆ push in on the child's diaphragm

    ◆ have him lie on his stomach on the floor propped on his elbows

    ◆ have him lie over a big ball as you hold him at the hips and push into the ball to bounce him

Tracking Sheet for Oral-Motor Stimulation

Name _____

Preparing for Speech for the /t, d, n/ sounds	Dates			
1. Whole Body Wake-Ups				
a. burst of movement				
b. sustained movement				
c. resistive sucking				
d. "Row Your Boat"				
2. Face Wake-Ups				
a. pats parts of face				
b. rub alveolus				
c. tap tongue tip and sides, lick teeth				
d. pull object between closed teeth				
3. Jaw Stability				
a. open/close mouth against resistance				
b. push in on chin				
c. rest chin in hands				
4. Vocal Warm-Ups				
a. isolated vowel productions				
b. vowel sequences				
c. tongue clicks				
d. other				
5. Taste and Food Activities				
a. _____				
b. _____				
c. _____				
6. Direct Facilitation Techniques				
a. rub tongue tip, central groove, sides, and alveolar ridge				
b. tap tongue tip and front				
c. resistance (push down on tongue, push into front of tip and sides)				
d. stroke central groove				
e. lick up food in front of mouth				
f. other techniques/cues				
_____				
_____				
_____				

Comments:

Activities

Give the child the worksheet and materials necessary to complete each activity. Practice each target sound, syllable, or word three times. Write target syllables or words on the worksheets or glue on word pictures. Provide all the cues the child needs to successfully produce the target sound. Send completed worksheets home for additional practice.

Materials needed for the /t, d, n/ worksheets:

- ◆ markers
- ◆ crayons
- ◆ pencil
- ◆ scissors
- ◆ tape

Activities for /t/

1. On the *Tickled Pink* worksheet, have the child say the /t/ sound in isolation and then color a stripe on the drum. When he's finished, have him color the tiger pink.

2. Write /t/ + vowel or vowel + /t/ syllable combinations on the *Tulip Garden* worksheet. Have the child say a syllable three times and then color a tulip.

3. Write initial /t/ words on the players' jerseys on the *Tip-Off Time* worksheet. Have the child say a word on a player's jersey three times and then color the jersey.

4. Write final /t/ words on the *Nat's Hat* worksheet. Have the child say a word three times and then draw a line to connect two of the dots.

5. Write medial /t/ words in the boxes on the *Lotto Board* worksheet. Have the child say a word in a box three times and then color the box until he gets five boxes in a row. Repeat to get another lotto.

6. Write multisyllabic /t/ words on the parrot's tail feathers on the *Parrot Talk* worksheet. Have the child say a word on a tail feather three times and then color it a bright color.

7. On the *Building a Soapbox Derby Car* worksheet, there are many /t/, /d/, and /n/ words pictured in all positions of words for additional practice or for phrase and sentence practice. After the child has identified and practiced the /t/ words, have him circle the pictures that have his target sound.

   The following /t/ words are targeted in this scene:

tacks	tools	two	eight	nut
tape	top	belt	hat	paint
ten	tube	bottom	hitting	seat
tire	twelve	cat	mallet	sister

Activities for /d/

1. On the *Don't Double Dribble* worksheet, have the child say the /d/ sound in isolation three times and then draw a basketball around an X.

2. Write /d/ + vowel or vowel + /d/ syllable combinations on the *Bugler's Day* worksheet. Have the child say a syllable three times and then color a musical note.

3. Write initial /d/ words on the butterflies on the *A Day Off* worksheet. Have the child say a word on a butterfly three times and then color the butterfly.

4. Write final /d/ words on the children's shirts on the *Mud Slide* worksheet. Have the child say a word on a child's shirt three times and then color the shirt.

5. On the *Calendar Time* worksheet, have the child say the days of the week. Write medial /d/ words on each square of the calendar. Have the child say a word on the calendar three times and then put an X on it.

6. Write multisyllabic /d/ words in the puddles on the *Puddle Jumping* worksheet. Have the child say each word three times and then color the picture.

7. On the *Building a Soapbox Derby Car* worksheet, there are many /t/, /d/, and /n/ words pictured in all positions of words for additional practice or for phrase and sentence practice. After the child has identified and practiced the /d/ words, have him circle the pictures that have his target sound.

   The following /d/ words are targeted in this scene:

dad	head
door	under
around	windshield
beside	

Activities for /n/

1. On the *Go Cars Go!* worksheet, have the child say the /n/ sound in isolation as he traces each car's path along the track. Then have the child color the car.

2. Write /n/ + vowel or vowel + /n/ syllable combinations on the *Mr. Ned* worksheet. Have the child say each syllable three times and then color Mr. Ned.

3. Write initial /n/ words under the newspaper on the *News Flash!* worksheet. Have the child say a word three times and then draw a picture in a box.

4. Write final /n/ words on the pins on *Pin It On* worksheet. Have the child say a word on a pin three times and then decorate the pin.

5. Write medial /n/ words on the train cars on the *Lionel's Tunnel* worksheet. Cut along the dotted lines on the tunnel. Cut out the train cars and tape them together.

   Put the train engine through the beginning of the tunnel. Have the child say the word written on it three times and then pull another car through the tunnel. After the child practices all the words, let him color the train.

6. Write multisyllabic /n/ words on the dragon on the *Napping Dragon* worksheet. Have the child say each word three times and then color the dragon.

7. On the *Building a Soapbox Derby Car* worksheet, there are many /t/, /d/, and /n/ words pictured in all positions of words for additional practice or for phrase and sentence practice. After the child has identified and practiced the /n/ words, have him circle the pictures that have his target sound.

   The following /n/ words are targeted in this scene:

nail	cabinet	eleven	seven
nine	can	in	ten
knee	children	lightning	under
afternoon			

Chapter 4
Velar Sounds /k, g/

> **How the /k, g/ sounds are made:**
> The back of the tongue is raised to contact the soft palate. Air pressure is built up behind the tongue and then released as the tongue moves toward the next articulated sound. The vocal folds are vibrating for the /g/ sound.

Preparing for Speech

After you prepare the child's body, face, and speech mechanism for speech practice, provide direct techniques for sound facilitation. Follow this with speech practice. Implement troubleshooting techniques as needed. Don't forget to wear protective gloves when working in or around a child's face and mouth.

Whole Body Wake-Ups

Have the child:

- ◆ do short burst of movement activities such as jumping, punching, skipping, bouncing, kicking, or squeezing/pounding Play-Doh.®

- ◆ drink a cool tart drink such as cranberry juice through a thin straw.

- ◆ do resistive movements such as pulling hard on a rope, carrying a heavy chair, or carrying a heavy box, crate, or basket of toys.

Face Wake-Ups

1. Have the child use her index and middle fingers to pat her cheeks, lips, and under her chin.

2. Make "snake" movements with the child by protruding and retracting your tongues rapidly several times.

3. Do blowing or resistive sucking activities.

Jaw Stability

Gently push downward on the chin as the child attempts to keep her mouth closed. Then, push upward while the child attempts to open her mouth (resistance).

Provide proprioceptive input by pushing inward on the point of the chin with deep pressure for a few seconds and/or massaging the muscles around the temporal-mandibular joint.

Vocal Warm-Ups

Have the child:

- ◆ imitate individual, sustained, long vowels.

- ◆ imitate vowel sequences.

- ◆ imitate funny sounds such as gulping, a frog croaking, a crow "kaw-kaw" sound, or a baby saying "goo-goo."

- ◆ gargle or cough.

Taste and Food Activities to Facilitate Tongue Retraction

1. Have the child chew foods like raisins or licorice between her molars.

2. Have the child bite celery or carrot sticks using her incisors to facilitate jaw grading.

3. Give the child a piece of peppermint, spearmint, or cinnamon gum to chew to alert the oral area.

Direct Techniques to Facilitate Sound Placement

Repeat each technique three times. Review the *Program Sequence*, *Program Guidelines*, and *Illustrated Oral-Motor Techniques* in the introductory pages as needed.

1. Using your index and middle fingers, "walk" back on the child's tongue or tap along the front half of her tongue along the midline. Try to avoid eliciting a gag reflex.

2. Rub the sides of the back half of the child's tongue, moving from front to back. Then, rub the insides of the back teeth along the gum edge. Have the child scrape the sides of her upper molars with the back sides of her tongue.

3. Put your finger on the top of the child's tongue at the back side margins and push down as the child pushes back. Repeat on the other side. Be careful not to elicit the gag reflex.

4. Put your finger along one edge of the back of the child's tongue and push into that side as the child pushes back. Repeat on the other side.

5. Put your finger or a tongue depressor just inside the child's lips. Have the child push against it using her tongue without moving her head (resistance).

6. Use a tongue depressor or your finger to press into the child's tongue tip as you push the bulk of her tongue back. This should elevate the back of the tongue.

Tips and Troubleshooting Techniques

For the child who has difficulty achieving or maintaining retraction and elevation of the back of the tongue:

1. Make the child aware of the physical characteristics of the sound. Use a verbal description or body movements.

2. Use touch cues to the child's face as she produces the target sound in isolation, syllables, or words. The touch should be under the child's chin just anterior to the neck, using a firmer touch for /g/. Use hand signals to further cue the child on /k/ and /g/ productions. (See pages 174-176 in the *Materials Book*.)

3. Check the lingual frenum for adequate length to achieve tongue retraction.

4. If persistent mouth breathing is present, check the child's tonsils and adenoids. Also check the muscle tone in her body, face, and tongue. Enlarged tonsils and adenoids may impede the airway and encourage a more tongue-forward positioning. The presence of allergies can also contribute to mouth breathing as can low muscle tone.

5. Try having the child lie on her back, using gravity to help retract her tongue. With her chin slightly tucked, press up on her neck at the base of her tongue as the child says the isolated sound.

6. Go from another sound such as from /h/ to /k/ or /ng/ to /g/.

7. If the child persists in substituting /t/ or /d/, check the position of her jaw. The child's teeth should be open slightly and the point of her chin should be in midline. Have her rest her chin on her hand or cup her chin in both hands to stabilize her jaw and to control the amount her mouth opens.

8. Cue her to use a "fatter" tongue. Do this verbally and by going from a sustained /i/ (as in "eat") which is a wide vowel to a /k/ or /g/ production.

9. While you press the child's tongue tip down and back, have the child attempt to produce a /t/ or /d/ sound.

10. Place a tongue depressor, finger, toothbrush bristles, or Infa-dent at the front of the child's tongue while her tongue is in her mouth and slightly retracted. Have the child retract her tongue away from the object without elevating her tongue tip. You can also lay the object on the front third of the child's tongue and have the child pull her tongue back and away without elevating the tip.

11. Put the end of a straw at the child's tongue tip and push into the tip to encourage tongue retraction.

12. If the child has difficulty with air release, press inward and upward at her diaphragm as she produces the sound. Hold a feather or small paper in front of her mouth so she can see the air release or have her feel the air with her hand.

13. If the child has difficulty getting enough pressure for the sound, have her press the knuckles of one hand into her palm or your palm with deep pressure, or have her press her palms together firmly and release as she produces the sound.

Tracking Sheet for Oral-Motor Stimulation

Name _____

Preparing for Speech for the /k, g/ sounds	Dates			
1. Whole Body Wake-Ups				
a. burst of movement				
b. drink cool tart drink, thin straw				
c. resistive movements				
2. Face Wake-Ups				
a. pats parts of face				
b. protrude and retract tongue rapidly				
c. blowing/sucking				
3. Jaw Stability				
a. open/close mouth against resistance				
b. push in on chin				
c. rest chin in hands				
4. Vocal Warm-Ups				
a. isolated vowel productions				
b. vowel sequences				
c. funny sounds: gulp, frog, crow, baby				
d. gargle, cough				
e. other				
5. Taste and Food Activities				
a. _____				
b. _____				
c. _____				
6. Direct Facilitation Techniques				
a. walk or tap on front half of tongue				
b. rub sides of tongue and alveolar ridge				
c. push down on top back sides of tongue				
d. push into back sides of tongue				
e. push tongue against finger				
f. press into tongue tip				
g. other techniques/cues				
_____				
_____				
_____				

Comments:

Activities

Give the child the worksheet and materials necessary to complete each activity. Practice each target sound, syllable, or word three times. Write target syllables or words on the worksheets or glue on word pictures. Provide all the cues the child needs to successfully produce the target sound. Send completed worksheets home for additional practice.

Materials needed for the /k, g/ worksheets:

- ◆ markers
- ◆ crayons
- ◆ pencil
- ◆ scissors
- ◆ glue

Activities for /k/

1. On the *Cackling Crows* worksheet, have the child say the /k/ sound in isolation three times and then color a crow.

2. Write /k/ + vowel or vowel + /k/ syllable combinations on the flags on the *Read the Code* worksheet. Have the child say a syllable on a flag three times and then color the flag.

3. Write initial /k/ words on the cards on the *Card Shark* worksheet. Have the child say a word on a card three times and then color the card.

4. Write final /k/ words on the *Nick Is Sick* worksheet. Have the child say each word three times and then color Nick.

5. Write medial /k/ words on the *Checkers King* worksheet. Have the child say each word on a checker three times and then color the checker red or black.

6. Write multisyllabic /k/ words on the horse's spots on the *Keesha the Bareback Rider* worksheet. Have the child say a word on one of the horse's spots three times and then color the spot. When all words have been practiced, have the child color Keesha's costume.

7. On the *Urban Hike* worksheet, there are many /k/ and /g/ words pictured in all positions of words for additional practice or for phrase and sentence practice. After the child has identified and practiced the /k/ words, have her circle the pictures that have her target sound.

   The following /k/ words are targeted in this scene:

cake	coat	bakery	sidewalk
canteen	crosswalk	bank	sneakers
cap	curb	bike	trash can
car	backpack	book (store)	truck

Activities for /g/

1. On the *For Good Measure* worksheet, have the child say the /g/ sound in isolation three times for each mark on the measuring cup and then color the cup so it looks full.

2. Write /g/ + vowel or vowel + /g/ syllable combinations on the frog's hats on the *A Frog Jig* worksheet. Have the child say a syllable on a hat three times and then color the frog.

3. Write initial /g/ words on the hockey pucks on the *Go For the Goal* worksheet. Have the child say each word on a hockey puck three times and then cut them out and glue them in the goal.

4. Write final /g/ words on the hogs on the *Hog Clog* worksheet. Have the child say a word on a hog three times and then color the hog.

5. Write medial /g/ words on the penguins on the *Penguin Wiggle* worksheet. Have the child say a word on a penguin three times and then color the penguin.

6. Write multisyllabic /g/ words on the planets on the *Galaxy Game* worksheet. After the child says a word on a planet three times, have her connect part of the line that takes the space shuttle from one planet to another on its way to the moon. When the child is finished practicing, the space shuttle should be connected to the moon. Let the child color the planets along the way.

7. On the *Urban Hike* worksheet, there are many /k/ and /g/ words pictured in all positions of words for additional practice or for phrase and sentence practice. After the child has identified and practiced the /g/ words, have her circle the pictures that have her target sound.

   The following /g/ words are targeted in this scene:

gate	bag	shaggy dog
girl	big	signal
guy	jog (jogger)	sleeping bag

Chapter 5
Lingua-alveolar Strident Sounds /s, z/

How /s/ and /z/ sounds are made:
The front of the tongue is near or in contact with the alveolar ridge and has a narrow central opening. The sides of the tongue are in contact with the upper gums and teeth. There is a central groove in the tongue. The jaw is nearly closed with the lips slightly spread. The air passes down the central groove of the tongue in a continuous stream. The vocal folds vibrate on the /z/.

Preparing for Speech

After you prepare the child's body, face, and speech mechanism for speech practice, provide direct techniques for sound facilitation. Follow this with speech practice. Implement troubleshooting techniques as needed. Don't forget to wear protective gloves when working in or around a child's face and mouth.

Whole Body Wake-Ups

Have the child:

♦ do long, sustained movements such as sliding, swinging, or pulling. You could use more flexion activities like a somersault if the child has a frontal lisp or has low tone, and more extension activities if he is using a backing or stopping pattern.

♦ do activities that facilitate respiration/breath support for speech such as sustained blowing. Have the child take a deep breath as he raises his arms over his head, then blow the air out in a long, easy expiration as he lowers his arms to his sides. Or have him lie over a big therapy ball or bolster and help him roll forward to touch his hands to the floor, then back to the starting position.

♦ wiggle or crawl on his stomach like a snake, or put his arms out and "fly" around the room like a bee (for younger children).

Face Wake-Ups

1. Using his fingers, have the child pat his cheeks, lips, and under his chin.

2. Use your index and middle fingers to apply manual vibration to the child's facial muscles. Start at the child's temples and vibrate the fingers on both sides of the child's face at the same time while moving slowly to the corner of his lips. Do this for each facial muscle going from point of origin to the point of insertion at the lips. (See page 21.) Then, vibrate around the lips beginning at the center of the child's upper lip and moving in a circle along the lips back to the starting point.

3. Increase awareness of the tongue parts as you name them. Stroke one side of the child's tongue from the tip to the back. Then, stroke the other side. Be sure to stroke the sides of the child's tongue and not the top of the sides. Stroke the top of the child's tongue along the tip and lateral margins. Finally, stroke the central groove of the child's tongue from the front to halfway back. Be careful not to elicit the gag reflex.

4. Using a gloved finger, Infa-dent, Toothette, or washcloth, stroke with deep pressure along the upper gum line behind the child's teeth from the right to the left molars. Repeat three times. This will desensitize the area for those children who are orally defensive.

Jaw Stability

Gently push downward on the child's chin as he attempts to keep his mouth closed. Then, push upward while the child attempts to open his mouth (resistance).

Provide proprioceptive input by pushing inward on the point of the chin with deep pressure for a few seconds and/or massaging the muscles around the temporal-mandibular joint.

Vocal Warm-Ups

Have the child:

◆ imitate vowels and vowel sequences. Use the vowel sequences /oo-ee/ and /oo-ay/ to get lip positioning.

◆ make long, sustained sounds such as "sssss" for a snake, "shhhhh" to tell others to be quiet, or a breathy sigh.

◆ whisper the nursery rhyme "Itsy Bitsy Spider" as you act it out. Exaggerate the strident sounds.

◆ whisper a message, make the sound of a leaky tire, or a teapot steam sound.

Taste and Food Activities to Facilitate Stridents

1. Have the child eat foods to "wake up" his mouth like Hot Tamales, War Heads candy, cinnamon chewing gum, or dill pickles.

2. Have the child bite and chew with his lips closed. Use foods such as crackers, celery or carrot sticks, or pepperoni slices to facilitate jaw grading.

3. Have the child drink thick liquids through a straw or use curly straws. Put the straw on the front central groove (midline of the tongue) when drinking. To facilitate tongue retraction, use a tart drink such as lemonade or cranberry juice with the curly straw.

4. Place a sticky food such as peanut butter, jelly, icing from a tube, or marshmallow cream on the center of the child's alveolar ridge. Have the child lick it off from front to back, using the tip of his tongue and the front of his tongue.

Direct Techniques to Facilitate Sound Placement

Repeat each technique three times. Review the *Program Sequence, Program Guidelines,* and *Illustrated Oral-Motor Techniques* in the introductory pages as needed.

There are several important factors that can affect placement and production of /s/ and /z/. Direct techniques for sound placement are listed in a general therapy progression to target these factors. Implement techniques to facilitate jaw stability, a central groove in the tongue, and elevation of the tongue tip and sides. Then, select techniques as needed for a frontal lisp, a lateral lisp, or for respiration/breath support for speech. Some techniques may target more than one problem area.

1. Facilitate jaw stability and graded jaw movements. Without jaw control, the tongue has difficulty moving independently to find and maintain a position for sound production. Jaw stability and control can be affected by overall body and facial muscle tone as well as by a habitual jaw-open position with mouth breathing.

   a. Have the child cup his chin in both hands or place his chin on his fist to provide jaw stability as he practices his target sounds and words.

   b. Have the child use a bite block such as a straw, thin pretzel, or coffee stirrer between his molars during speech tasks.

   c. Improve jaw grading by biting crackers, carrot sticks, or celery sticks.

2. Facilitate a central groove in the midline of the tongue to get tongue placement and proper air flow. The central groove is needed for the passage of the airstream. When it is absent or reduced, the child omits the strident or substitutes a stop or a lateral production for the /s/ and /z/.

   a. Using a gloved finger, apply a deep pressure stroke along the central groove of the child's tongue from the tip back to the center. Do not elicit the gag reflex.

   b. Put a thin straw, a flat blunt toothpick, or a coffee stirrer on the front quarter of the central groove of the child's tongue. Have the child produce a prolonged /s/. Slowly pull the object out as the child continues to produce the sound.

3. Facilitate elevation of the tongue tip and sides. An elevated tongue tip with a central groove, and a front opening for air flow is needed, although some children may be more successful with their tongue tip lowered. Without elevation of the sides of the tongue, the strident may become a stop or may be lateralized.

   a. Using your gloved finger or texture such as an Infa-dent, Toothette, or washcloth, rub the child's alveolar ridge and tongue where contact is made between the two. Name the parts as you touch them.

   b. Using your gloved finger, stroke the sides of the tip of the child's tongue. Begin at the center of the tip and stroke about a quarter of the way back on each side.

71

    c. Place your gloved finger tip against the child's tongue tip and press into it. Follow by pushing into the tongue tip with the child attempting to push your finger away with his tongue without moving his head.

    d. Place your gloved finger on top of the child's tongue tip. Push down on the tongue as the child pushes up.

    e. Stroke the top sides of the child's tongue along the margins from the tip to the back (first stroking one side, then the other).

    f. Place your gloved finger beside the entire length of the side of the tongue. Push into the side of the tongue. Repeat on the other side. Do again and have the child push back with his tongue.

    g. Place your finger along the entire length of the top of the side of the tongue. Push down as the child attempts to push up without moving his head.

4. Counteract excessive tongue protrusion (frontal lisp). The tongue needs to be retracted behind the central incisors.

    a. Apply central groove techniques from above.

    b. Tap the tongue tip using short, quick taps along the central groove from the tongue tip to the center of the tongue.

    c. Use a bite block to stabilize the jaw and maintain jaw opening without shifting or excessive opening. (Be sure to check for 90°-90°-90° positioning as body position can affect jaw control. You want the back straight and the head in midline with the chin slightly tucked.) Apply other jaw stability and control techniques as needed.

    d. Stroke the child's tongue on the midline from the center to the tip.

    e. Grasp the child's tongue with a washcloth, pull it forward and briefly hold it.

    f. Elevate the child's tongue using your finger or a tongue blade and vibrate on either side of the lingual frenum.

    g. Apply tongue tip and side elevation techniques from above.

5. Counteract lateral emission of airflow (lateralized production). The sides of the tongue must be elevated and there must be a central groove for airflow for a non-lateralized strident production.

    a. Apply central groove techniques from above. In a lateral production, the air tends to flow over the sides of the tongue rather than down the central groove.

    b. Apply tongue tip and side elevation techniques from above. Emphasize elevation of the sides of the tongue.

    c. Use a bite block to stabilize the jaw and maintain jaw opening without shifting or excessive opening. (Be sure to check for 90°-90°-90° positioning as body position can affect jaw control. You want the back straight and the head in midline with the chin slightly tucked.) Apply other jaw stability and control techniques as needed.

d. Direct the child to blow the air on his central incisors to keep the air stream directed frontally, rather than laterally.

e. Put a straw on the front half of the central groove of the child's tongue. Have the child produce a sustained /s/ as you slowly pull the straw out.

6. Facilitate respiration/air support for speech. Without appropriate air support for speech, the strident may become an omission or stop and there may be cluster or syllabication reduction.

a. See techniques under **Whole Body Wake-Ups**, page 69.

b. Do blowing activities that require sustained breath.

c. Have the child lie on her stomach, propped on her elbows during speech production with her head forward and up, not sunk between her shoulders.

d. Have the child produce sustained vowels, a continuous vowel sequence, or sustained vowels while gliding into a strident production.

e. Push into the child's diaphragm as he produces the strident sound.

f. Do exercises that facilitate breath control such as jumping, bouncing, running, or doing sit-ups.

g. Have the child lie face down over a large therapy ball. Hold the child at the hips and push into the ball as you bounce him.

h. Check the child's body muscle tone for low tone or a bent/slumped body positioning.

Tips and Troubleshooting Techniques

For the child who has difficulty achieving or maintaining a tongue elevation placement:

1. Make the child aware of the physical characteristics of the sound (long sustained sound). Use a verbal description or body movements.

2. Use touch cues to the child's face as he produces the target sound in isolation, syllables, or words. Put a finger on the top center of the child's upper lip using deep pressure. Pull your finger away from the child to signal airflow. Pull away in a zigzag motion for /z/. Use hand signals to cue the child to use an elevated tongue placement for the /s/ or /z/. (See pages 174-176 in the *Materials Book*.)

3. Go from another sound placement to the /s/ or /z/. Use smooth, prolonged productions in which one sound blends into the next. Do not pause between the sounds.

    a. Start with /t/ and go to a prolonged /s/ ("tssss").

    b. Start with voiceless /th/ and go to /s/ or voiced /th/ to /z/. Slowly retract the tongue from the /th/ to the /s/ or /z/ while sustaining airflow.

    c. Start with /i/ ("eee") and go to /s/ to get tongue spreading with the sides of the tongue in contact with the teeth.

    d. Start with /sh/ and slowly move the tongue forward to /s/ while sustaining the air flow.

    e. Start with /di/ or /bi/ ("dee" or "bee") and go to /z/ to get voicing. Say words like *dees* or *bees*.

4. Place a small piece of paper, a feather, or a light ball in front of the child's mouth to illustrate air flow as he says the sound.

5. Check for mouth breathing, habitual jaw-open posture, poor muscle tone or posture, and enlarged tonsils and adenoids, all of which can contribute to inaccurate articulator placement. Make sure the child is seated in the 90°-90°-90° position with his head in midline and his chin slightly tucked.

6. Orthodontic problems can contribute to jaw instability. Make sure the child closes or approximates his teeth in a normal occlusion. A cue is to hold an imaginary apple in front of the child and tell him to "take a bite." His teeth should close in a natural position. Do not let the jaw jut forward or lateralize. When the child achieves normal occlusion at the molars, press up under his chin to maintain the position and to give feedback. Don't let his head tilt back. A bite block can be useful in achieving jaw stability during sound production.

7. Have the child smile slightly to spread his lips and facilitate tongue spreading.

8. If the child produces a stop sound between the /s/ or /z/ and the rest of the word, have him elongate the strident and pause slightly following the /s/ or /z/ to give the articulators time to make adjustments ("ssss (pause) ock").

9. If the child substitutes a stop sound for the continuant:

   a. Check jaw stability and use a bite block as needed.

   b. Work on central groove of the tongue.

   c. Try an alternate placement with the tongue tip down.

   d. Work on elevation and spreading of the lateral margins of the tongue.

   e. Work on respiration and breath support for speech.

   f. Use a tactile or visual cue to illustrate the continuant. Stroke the child's arm from shoulder to hand while producing the /s/ or /z/, or stretch the child's hands apart while he sustains the continuant.

   g. Go from voiceless /th/ to /s/ or voiced /th/ to /z/. Encourage the child to slowly retract his tongue from /th/ to /s/ or /z/ while sustaining airflow. You might also start with /h/ and go to /s/ which may encourage appropriate airflow and lighter contact.

   h. Begin syllable practice with VC productions.

   i. Use forward or backward chaining techniques. Backward chaining is useful for prevocalic productions and forward chaining is useful for postvocalic productions. For forward chaining, have the child say the target word, omit the postvocalic /s/ or /z/, then add the strident ("bu, bu, bu, bus."). For backward chaining, have the child say the target /s/ or /z/ word while omitting the prevocalic /s/ or /z/ and then add the strident ("ock, ock, ock, sock").

10. To get voicing, go from another voiced sound to the /z/, lower the pitch for /z/, or go from humming to the /z/. Have the child feel the vibration of the larynx during voicing.

Tracking Sheet for Oral-Motor Stimulation

Name _____

Preparing for Speech for the /sh, ch, j/ sounds	Dates			
1. Whole Body Wake-Ups				
a. sustained movement – /sh/				
b. sustained blowing				
c. respiration/breath support				
d. snake wiggle or bee flying				
2. Face Wake-Ups				
a. pats parts of face				
b. manual vibration to facial musles				
c. stroke tongue to increase awareness of parts				
d. stroke molar to molar along upper gum line				
3. Jaw Stability				
a. open/close mouth against resistance				
b. push in on chin				
c. rest chin in hands/on fist				
d. bite block				
4. Vocal Warm-Ups				
a. isolated vowel productions				
b. vowel sequences				
c. sustained /s/, /sh/, sigh				
d. whispered message, tire, or teapot sounds				
5. Taste and Food Activities				
a. _____				
b. _____				
c. _____				
6. Direct Facilitation Techniques				
a. stroke tongue/straw on central groove				
b. stroke tongue and alveolar ridge				
c. stroke sides of tongue tip				
d. press into /down on tongue tip				
e. stroke top sides of tongue				
f. push into tongue sides				
g. push down on top of tongue sides				
h. counteract tongue protrusion				
i. counteract lateral air emission				
j. facilitate respiration/air support				
k. other techniques/cues				
_____				
_____				
_____				

Comments:

Activities

Give the child the worksheet and materials necessary to complete each activity. Practice each target sound, syllable, or word three times. Write target syllables or words on the worksheets or glue on word pictures. Provide all the cues the child needs to successfully produce the target sound. Send completed worksheets home for additional practice.

Materials needed for the /s, z/ worksheets:

- ◆ markers
- ◆ crayons
- ◆ pencil
- ◆ colored paper
- ◆ scissors
- ◆ glue

Activities for the /s/ sound

1. On the *Seta Stops the Leaks* worksheet, have the child say the /s/ sound in isolation and then draw a patch on each leak on the float.

2. Write /s/ + vowel or vowel + /s/ syllable combinations on the quilt on the *See Sue Sew* worksheet. Have the child say each syllable three times and then color a square on the quilt.

3. Write initial /s/ words in the flags on the *Sam Sails Away* worksheet and cut them out. Have the child say a word on a flag three times and then glue the flag on the sailboat. When all the flags are glued on, have the child color them.

4. Write final /s/ words on the barn on the *Moose Lodge* worksheet. Have the child say a word three times and then color a moose.

5. Write medial /s/ words on the *The Icing on the Cake* worksheet. Have the child say a word on a layer of cake three times and then decorate the layer.

6. Cut out some strips of colored paper the size of the stripes on the lighthouse on the *Salty's Lighthouse* worksheet. Write multisyllabic /s/ words on the strips. Have the child practice a word on a strip three times and then glue the strip on a section of the lighthouse.

7. On the *Tending the Garden* worksheet, there are many /s/ and /z/ words pictured in all positions of words for additional practice or for phrase and sentence practice. After the child has identified and practiced the /s/ words, have him circle the pictures that have his target sound.

   The following /s/ words are targeted in this scene:

seat	sunhat	bracelet	pots
summer	basket	face	tennis shoes
sun	beside	faucet	
sunglasses	birdhouse	lettuce	

Activities for the /z/ sound

1. On the *Zip Down Z Slide* worksheet, have the child say the /z/ sound in isolation and draw a line from one dot to the next until he gets to the end of the slide. Then, have the child color the inner tubes.

2. Write /z/ + vowel or vowel + /z/ syllable combinations on the jacket on the *Zip 'Em Up* worksheet. Have the child say a syllable three times and then color a zipper on the jacket.

3. Write initial /z/ words on the *Animal Zap* worksheet. Have the child say a word on the page three times and then draw a net over one of the animals in the game. Write the score in the box, 10 points for each animal captured.

4. Write final /z/ words on the ribbons on the *Prize Winners* worksheet. Have the child say a word on a ribbon three times and then color the ribbon.

5. Write medial /z/ words on the *Mr. Weasel and His Easel* worksheet. Have the child say each word three times and then draw a picture on the canvas.

6. Write multisyllabic /z/ words on the *Does the Piece Fit?* worksheet. Have the child draw in a piece of the puzzle as she practices each word three times. When the puzzle is complete, have the child draw a picture on the puzzle.

7. On the *Tending the Garden* worksheet, there are many /s/ and /z/ words pictured in all positions of words for additional practice or for phrase and sentence practice. After the child has identified and practiced the /z/ words, have him circle the pictures that have his target sound.

   The following /z/ words are targeted in this scene:

zinnia	butterflies	flowers	roses
zucchini	daisy	hose	stems
bees	degrees	leaves	waters
bows	eyes	nose	

Chapter 6
Palatal Sounds /sh, ch, j/

How the /sh/ sound is made:
The front of the tongue is up and drawn slightly back and the sides of the tongue, including the back lateral margins, are against the juncture of the teeth and alveolar ridge. The tongue is broader and there is a larger opening at the front of the tongue than there is for the /s/ sound. The lips are protruded, somewhat rounded, and drawn in at the corners. There is a slight central groove in the tongue. The teeth are lightly touching or slightly separated.

How the /ch/ and /j/ sounds are made:
The tongue front is up and in contact with the hard palate, just behind the placement for /t/. All of the margins of the tongue are in contact with either the palate or the teeth to block the air flow. The tip releases and the air explodes. The lips are slightly protruded and rounded. The teeth are almost closed. The vocal folds are vibrating for the /j/ sound.

Preparing for Speech

After you prepare the child's body, face, and speech mechanism for speech practice, provide direct techniques for sound facilitation. Follow this with speech practice. Implement troubleshooting techniques as needed. Don't forget to wear protective gloves when working in or around a child's face and mouth.

Whole Body Wake-Ups

Have the child:

- ◆ do long, sustained movements such as sliding, swinging, pulling, carrying something heavy like a therapy ball, a chair, or a basket of toys for /sh/.

- ◆ do breath support/respiration activities. Have the child take a deep breath as she raises her arms over her head, then blow the air out in a long, easy expiration as she lowers her arms to her sides. Or have her lie over a big therapy ball or bolster and help her roll forward to touch her hands to the floor, then back to the starting position.

- ◆ do short-burst-of-air activities such as jumping, punching, skipping, bouncing, or kicking for /ch/ and /j/.

- ◆ do resistive movements such as isometric exercises. Have the child push against a wall or have her place her hands together at the waist, palm to palm, and push her hands together in short bursts of pressure.

Face Wake-Ups

1. Use your index and middle fingers to apply manual vibration to the child's facial muscles. Start at the temples and vibrate your fingers on both sides of the child's face at the same time

while moving slowly to the corners of the lips. Do this for each facial muscle, going from point of origin to the point of insertion at the lips. (See illustration on page 21.) Vibrate around the child's lips, beginning at the center of the upper lip and moving in a circle around the lips.

2. Have the child use an exaggerated pucker to throw kisses or to make "fish faces" by opening and closing her rounded lips.

3. Have the child do blowing activities with rounded lips. (See pages 30-31 for suggested activities.)

4. Have the child do resistive sucking activities such as sucking thicker liquids through a straw or using a curly straw.

5. Use a gloved finger, Infa-dent, Toothette, or washcloth to rub along the inside of the child's upper gums behind her teeth from molar to molar three times. Tap the center of the child's tongue, moving from front to back. Stroke the tongue along the sides from the tip to the back. Do not elicit a gag reflex. Name the parts you touch to increase the child's awareness.

Jaw Stability

Gently push downward on the child's chin as she attempts to keep her mouth closed. Then, push upward while the child attempts to open her mouth.

Provide proprioceptive input by pushing inward on the point of the child's chin with deep pressure for a few seconds and/or massaging the muscles around the temporal-mandibular joint.

Vocal Warm-Ups

Have the child:

- ◆ imitate vowels and vowel sequences.
- ◆ click her tongue using independent tongue movements, without moving her jaw.
- ◆ make funny sounds such as a whistle, a whooshing sound, or a wind sound.

Taste and Food Activities to Facilitate Palatal Sounds

1. Have the child bite crackers or celery and carrot sticks for jaw gradation.

2. Have the child chew foods that will "wake up" her mouth such as cinnamon chewing gum, Hot Tamales candy, Sour Patch Kids candy, War Heads, or dill pickles.

3. Place a sticky food such as peanut butter, jelly, icing from a tube, or marshmallow cream on the child's palate right behind her alveolar ridge. Have the child lick it off from front to back using her tongue tip and the front of her tongue.

Direct Techniques to Facilitate Sound Placement

Repeat each technique three times. Review the *Program Sequence, Program Guidelines*, and *Illustrated Oral-Motor Techniques* in the introductory pages as needed.

There are several important factors that can affect placement and production of /sh, ch/ and /j/. Direct techniques for sound placement are listed in a general therapy progression to target these factors. Implement techniques to facilitate jaw stability, a central groove in the tongue, and elevation of the tongue tip and sides. Then select techniques as needed to target a frontal or lateral production, or respiration/breath support for speech. Some techniques may target more than one problem area.

1. Facilitate jaw stability and graded jaw movements. Without this control, the tongue has difficulty moving independently to find and maintain a position for sound production. Jaw positioning, stability, and control can be affected by overall body positioning and body and facial muscle tone as well as by a habitual jaw-open position with mouth breathing.

   a. Have the child cup her chin in both hands, or place her chin on her fist to provide jaw stability as she practices target sounds and words.

   b. Use a bite block such as a straw, thin pretzel, or coffee stirrer between the molars during speech tasks.

   c. Facilitate jaw grading by having the child bite crackers, carrot sticks, or celery sticks.

2. Facilitate a central groove in the midline of the tongue to get tongue placement and proper air flow. Central grooving is needed for the airstream passage. When it is absent or reduced, the child will omit the strident or will substitute a stop or a lateral production.

   a. Using a gloved finger, stroke along the central groove of the child's tongue from the tip back to the center of the tongue. Do not elicit a gag reflex.

   b. Put a thin straw, a flat blunt toothpick, or a coffee stirrer on the front of the central groove. To get the airstream down the groove, have the child produce a prolonged /s/ or /sh/ with the object on the central groove. Then, slowly pull the object out as the child continues to produce the sound.

3. Facilitate elevation of the tongue tip and sides and spreading of the tongue. An elevated tongue tip with a central groove and a front opening for air flow is needed. Without spreading and elevation of the sides of the tongue, the production may be a stop or lateral production.

   a. Using your gloved finger, stroke the sides of the tip of the child's tongue. Begin at the tip and stroke about a quarter of the way back on each side of the tongue.

   b. Place your gloved finger tip against the child's tongue tip and press into it. Repeat but have the child push back to provide resistance without moving her head.

    c. Place your gloved finger on top of the child's tongue tip. Push down on the tongue as the child pushes up.

    d. Stroke the top sides of the child's tongue from the tip to the back. First stroke one side, then the other.

    e. Place your gloved finger beside the entire length of the side of the child's tongue. Push into the side of the tongue. Repeat on the other side. Repeat and have the child push back with her tongue.

    f. Place your gloved finger along the entire length of the top of the side of the tongue. Push down as the child attempts to push up without moving her head.

    g. Using a standard size Y-shaped dental floss holder with no floss, put the Y behind the top front teeth and encourage the child to spread her tongue so that it is touching both sides of the holder. The holder can be used to gently guide the tongue into position.

    h. Encourage elevation of the back sides of the tongue using techniques d, e, and f.

4. Counteract excessive tongue protrusion (interdental placement). The tongue needs to be retracted behind the central incisors.

    a. Apply central groove techniques from above (#2).

    b. Tap the tongue tip using short quick taps along the central groove from the tongue tip to the center of the tongue.

    c. Use a bite block to stabilize the jaw and maintain jaw opening without shifting or excessive opening. Be sure to check for 90°-90°-90° positioning as body position can affect jaw positioning and control. The child's back should be straight and her head in midline with her chin slightly tucked. Apply other jaw stability and control techniques as needed.

    d. Grasp the tongue with a washcloth, pull it forward, and briefly hold it.

    e. Elevate the tongue and use your gloved finger or a tongue blade to vibrate on either side of the lingual frenum.

    f. Apply tongue tip and side elevation techniques from above (#3).

5. Counteract lateral emission of airflow (lateralized production). The sides of the tongue must be elevated and there must be a central groove for airflow for a non-lateralized strident production.

    a. Apply central groove techniques from above.

    b. Apply tongue tip and side elevation techniques from above. Emphasize elevation of the sides of the tongue.

82

    c. Use a bite block to stabilize the jaw and maintain jaw opening without shifting or excessive opening. Be sure to check for 90°-90°-90° positioning as body position can affect jaw control. The child's back should be straight and her head in midline with her chin slightly tucked. Apply other jaw stability and control techniques as needed.

    d. Direct the child to blow the air on her central incisors to keep the airstream directed frontally, rather than laterally.

    e. Have the child produce a sustained /s/ and push the tongue back to /sh/ using the tip of a straw or a tongue blade.

    f. Put a straw on the front half of the central groove of the child's tongue. Have her produce a sustained /sh/ as you slowly pull the straw out.

6. Facilitate respiration/air support for speech. Without appropriate air support for speech, the strident may become an omission or stop and there may be syllabication reduction.

    a. See techniques under **Whole Body Wake-Ups,** page 79.

    b. Do blowing activities that require sustained breath.

    c. Have the child lie on her stomach, propped on her elbows during speech production.

    d. Have the child produce sustained vowels, a continuous vowel sequence, or sustained vowels while gliding into a strident production.

    e. Push into the child's diaphragm as she produces the strident sound.

    f. Do exercises that facilitate breath control such as jumping, bouncing, running, or sit-ups.

    g. Have the child lie face down over a large therapy ball. Hold the child at the hips and push into the ball as you bounce her.

    h. Check the body muscle tone for low tone or a bent/slumped body positioning.

Tips and Troubleshooting Techniques

For the child who has difficulty achieving or maintaining tongue elevation and spreading:

1. Make the child aware of the physical characteristics of the sound (short popping sound or long sustained sound). Use a verbal description or body movements.

2. Use touch cues to the child's face such as stroking or circling a gloved finger around the outside of the child's lips as he produces the target sound in isolation, syllables, or words. Use a light stroke for /sh/, a deeper stroke for /ch/, and a tapping stroke for /j/. Use hand signals to cue the child to use a tongue-up and spread placement for the palatal sounds. (See pages 174-176 in the *Materials Book*.)

3. Check the lingual frenum for adequate length for tongue elevation.

4. Increase awareness of the lateral margins of the child's tongue and the tongue tip by rubbing them with a cotton swab dipped in mouthwash.

5. Increase lip tension to facilitate rounding.

    a. Have the child do blowing activities.

    b. Have the child do resistive sucking.

    c. Use your index finger and middle finger to apply manual vibration to the child's facial muscles, particularly around the lips.

    d. Provide stretch to the child's upper and lower lips. Starting from the midline of the child's top lip, stroke and stretch the lip from the center to the corners using deep pressure. Hold the stretch briefly at the corner of the mouth, then release. Repeat for the lower lip.

    e. Have the child say "eeee" or smile while you gently try to push her lips into a pucker (resistance).

    f. Have the child hold a pucker while you gently try to pull her lips into a smile (resistance).

    g. Have the child put her index finger in front of her lips while saying /sh/. This cue can often pull the lips forward and round them as well as help the child get correct tongue position.

6. If the child is having difficulty producing /sh/, /ch/, or /j/, go from another sound production to the palatal sounds.

    a. In a continuous progression, have the child go from voiceless /th/ to /s/ to /sh/ (i.e., slowly retract his tongue from the /th/ to the /s/ and /sh/ while sustaining airflow).

b. Have the child go from /s/ to /sh/ as she rounds her lips. If necessary, use gloved fingers to push the child's lips into position. Start with /sh/ or /t/ and go to /ch/, or from /sh/ or /d/ to /j/.

c. Have the child go from /t/ to /sh/, putting the sounds closer and closer together to get the plosive for /ch/.

d. Have the child produce the /t/ sound. Then, have her put her tongue in position for the /t/ sound again. Push her tongue back with a tongue depressor as she says /t/ in order to produce the /ch/ sound.

7. Have the child catch the back sides of her tongue between her molars and gently bite down. While maintaining the bite, have the child push her tongue up against her top molars. Then have her blow air for the /sh/ sound. Modify jaw position and lip rounding as needed. Go from the /sh/ position to /ch/ and /j/ productions.[1]

8. If the child lateralizes a palatal sound, work on increased lip rounding, central grooving of the tongue, elevation of the lateral margins of the tongue, and jaw position and stability.

9. If the child uses a stop for a continuant, work on placement of the sides of the tongue, air flow, and the central grooving and opening at the front of the tongue.

10. Look for 90°-90°-90° body positioning with the child's head in midline and her chin slightly tucked.

11. If the child isn't getting enough air build-up for the sounds or isn't getting a good plosive air release on /ch/ or /j/, work on respiration and breath support as she produces the sound.

   a. Push in on the child's diaphragm.

   b. Have the child lie on her stomach on the floor, propped up on her elbows with her head up and forward, not sunk between her shoulders.

   c. Have the child lie over a big therapy ball as you hold her at the hips and push into the ball to bounce her.

   d. Have the child jump or hop.

[1] Pamela Marshalla, Two-Day Workshop. *Oral-Motor Techniques in Articulation Therapy.* April 1994.

Tracking Sheet for Oral-Motor Stimulation

Name _____

Preparing for Speech for the /sh, ch, j/ sounds	Dates			
1. Whole Body Wake-Ups				
a. sustained movement – /sh/				
b. breath support/respiration				
c. burst of air – /ch/ and /j/				
d. resistive movement				
2. Face Wake-Ups				
a. manual vibration to facial muscles				
b. kiss/fish face with exaggerated pucker				
c. blowing/resistive sucking				
d. rub aveolus from molar to molar				
3. Jaw Stability				
a. open/close mouth against resistance				
b. push in on chin				
c. rest chin in hands/on fist				
d. bite block				
4. Vocal Warm-Ups				
a. isolated vowel productions				
b. vowel sequences				
c. tongue clicks				
d. funny sounds: whistle, whoosh, wind				
5. Taste and Food Activities				
a. _____				
b. _____				
c. _____				
6. Direct Facilitation Techniques				
a. stroke tongue/straw on central groove				
b. stroke sides of tongue tip				
c. press into/down on tongue tip				
d. stroke top sides of tongue				
e. push into tongue sides				
f. push down on top of tongue sides				
g. dental floss holder				
h. counteract tongue protrusion				
i. counteract lateral air emission				
j. facilitate respiration/air flow				
k. other techniques/cues				
_____				
_____				
_____				

Comments:

Activities

Give the child the worksheet and materials necessary to complete each activity. Practice each target sound, syllable, or word three times. Write target syllables or words on the worksheets or glue on word pictures. Provide all the cues the child needs to successfully produce the target sound. Send completed worksheets home for additional practice.

Materials needed for the /sh, ch, j/ worksheets:

- markers
- crayons
- cotton balls
- tissue paper

- pencil
- scissors
- glue
- construction paper

Activities for the /sh/ sound

1. On the *Sharon the Librarian* worksheet, have the child say the /sh/ sound in isolation three times and then draw a book in the hand of a child until everyone has one or two books.

2. Write /sh/ + vowel or vowel + /sh/ syllable combinations on the sheep on the *Counting Sheep* worksheet. Have the child say a syllable three times and then glue a cotton ball (or a wadded ball of tissue paper) on a sheep.

3. Write initial /sh/ words on the packages on the *Shop 'Til You Drop* worksheet. Have the child say the word on a package three times and then draw something in the package.

4. Write final /sh/ words on the water tub on the *Splish, Splash!* worksheet. Have the child say a word on the tub three times and then put an X on each dirt spot on the elephant. When the child is finished practicing, have him color all the water blue.

5. Write medial /sh/ words on the shells on the *Seashells on the Seashore* worksheet. Have the child say a word on a shell three times and then draw a line from the seashell to the girl's bag.

6. Write multisyllabic /sh/ words on the wishing well on the *Lucky Wishing Well* worksheet and cut out the pennies at the bottom of the page. Have the child say a word on the well three times and then glue a penny in the wishing well.

7. On the *Yard Sale* worksheet, there are many /sh/, /ch/, and /j/ words pictured in all positions of words for additional practice or for phrase and sentence practice. After the child has identified and practiced the /sh/ words, have her circle the pictures that have her target sound.

   The following /sh/ words are targeted in this scene:

shaggy dog	bushes	goldfish
shirt	cushion	lampshade
shoes	dishes	trash can

Activities for the /ch/ sound

1. On the *Chugging Along* worksheet, have the child say the /ch/ sound three times in isolation and then color three boards on the train track.

2. Write /ch/ + vowel or vowel + /ch/ syllable combinations on the *Chip Off the Old Block* worksheet. Have the child say a syllable three times and then color a chip of wood. When all the chips are colored, have the child describe what she thinks the sculpture will be.

3. Write initial /ch/ words on the books on the *Check It Out* worksheet. Have the child say a word on a book three times and then color the book.

4. On the *Make a Match* worksheet, write or draw the same practice word on two cards. Repeat for four other words so you have five pairs of cards. Have the child draw a line between the matching words each time she practices a final /ch/ word. When all the words have been practiced, have the child color the pairs to match.

5. Cut out the beachballs at the bottom of the *Beachball Lotto* worksheet. Write a medial /ch/ word on each ball and turn it face down. Write the same words in each Lotto square.

   Have the child choose a ball and say the word on it three times. Then, have the child glue the ball on the square on the board with the same word. When she gets three balls in a row, she wins the game. See how many lottos she can make.

6. Cut out 2" x 10" strips of construction paper and write multisyllabic /ch/ words on them. Show the child the *Chain Gang* worksheet and tell her that she will be making a chain like the children in the picture. Have the child make her own chain by adding a link made of a strip of construction paper each time she practices a word three times.

   Then, have her say the words again and color the paper chain on the worksheet. For more practice, have her draw additional links on the worksheet chain as she says each word.

7. On the *Yard Sale* worksheet, there are many /sh/, /ch/, and /j/ words pictured in all positions of words for additional practice or for phrase and sentence practice. After the child has identified and practiced the /ch/ words, have her circle the pictures that have her target sound.

   The following /ch/ words are targeted in this scene:

chair	lunch box
checkers	patch
couch	sandwich
furniture	

Activities for the /j/ sound

1. On the *Jack and Jill* worksheet, cut out Jack and Jill. Have the child move the figures from leaf to leaf as she says the /j/ sound in isolation three times. When Jack and Jill reach the top, have the child color the beanstalk.

2. Write /j/ + vowel or vowel + /j/ syllable combinations on the people's shirts on the *Jazz Time* worksheet. Have the child say a syllable on a shirt three times and then color the shirt.

3. Write initial /j/ words on the *Jungle Jim* worksheet. Have the child say one of the words on the sheet three times and then color a ring on the monkey bars.

4. Write final /j/ words on the stagecoach on the *Stagecoach Ride* worksheet. Have the child say a word on the stagecoach three times and then draw a face in one of the windows.

5. Write medial /j/ words on the big pillow on the *Pajama Party* worksheet. Have the child say a word on the pillow three times and then color a feather.

6. Write multisyllabic /j/ words on the *Gene the Giraffe* worksheet. Have the child say a word three times and then draw a spot on the giraffe. When he is fully spotted, have the child color the giraffe.

7. On the *Yard Sale* worksheet, there are many /sh/, /ch/, and /j/ words pictured in all positions of words for additional practice or for phrase and sentence practice. After the child has identified and practiced the /j/ words, have her circle the pictures that have her target sound.

   The following /j/ words are targeted in this scene:

gerbil	jokes	cage	teenager
giraffe	jump rope	fire engine	zoology
jeans	banjo	luggage	
jewelry	biology	refrigerator	

Chapter 7
Lingua-alveolar Glide Sound /l/

> How the /l/ sound is made:
> The tip of the tongue is somewhat broad and pressed lightly against the alveolar ridge.
> Or the tongue tip may be down slightly with the blade in contact with the alveolar ridge.
> There is a slight opening between the sides of the tongue and the teeth for voiced air flow.
> The lips are relaxed, approaching the position of the adjacent vowel. The amount of jaw
> opening is also influenced by the vowel.

Preparing for Speech

After you prepare the child's body, face, and speech mechanism for speech practice, provide direct
techniques for sound facilitation. Follow this with speech practice. Implement troubleshooting
techniques as needed. Don't forget to wear protective gloves when working in or around a child's
face and mouth.

Whole Body Wake-Ups

Have the child:

- perform short burst-of-air activities such as jumping, punching, hopping, skipping,
  bouncing, pounding, or kicking.

- do resistive sucking by using a straw in a thick drink, or using a curly straw.

- do resistive movements such as isometric exercises. Have the child push against a wall
  or have him place his hands together at his waist, palm to palm, and push his hands
  together in short bursts of pressure.

Face Wake-Ups

1. Have the child use his index and middle fingers to pat his cheeks, lips, and under his chin.

2. Have the child "clean his teeth" by licking his upper teeth from molar to molar with his
   tongue between his gums and his lip.

3. Put a sticky food such as peanut butter, jelly, or marshmallow cream above the center of the
   child's upper lip. Have the child lick it off the outside of her lip with her tongue.

4. Use a gloved finger, an Infa-dent, Toothette, pretzel, or carrot stick to rub along the child's
   upper gums behind his teeth from the left lateral incisor to the right one. Repeat three times.

Jaw Stability

Gently push downward on the child's chin as he attempts to keep his mouth closed. Next, push upward on the child's chin while he attempts to open his mouth. Then, have the child open his mouth while you try to close it by pushing upward on his chin.

Provide proprioceptive input by pushing inward on the point of the chin with deep pressure for a few seconds and/or massaging the muscles around the temporal-mandibular joint.

Vocal Warm-Ups

Have the child:

 ◆ imitate vowels and vowel sequences.

 ◆ click his tongue several times. Make sure the jaw is stabilized and the tongue is moving independently.

 ◆ imitate syllable strings using /t/, /d/, or /n/ like "tuh-tuh-tuh." Make sure the tongue tip is up and contacting the alveolus during these productions.

Taste and Food Activities to Facilitate Tongue Elevation

1. Have the child chew a piece of cinnamon, peppermint, or spearmint gum to ready the oral area. Have him chew and then hold the gum against his alveolar ridge with his tongue tip for a few seconds. Repeat. This can also be done with a hot (not sour) candy such as Hot Tamales or War Heads.

2. Have the child bite crackers or carrot and celery sticks to facilitate jaw grading ability.

3. Place a small amount of a sticky food such as peanut butter, jelly, or marshmallow cream on the center of the child's alveolar ridge and palate. Have the child use the front of his tongue to lick from the alveolus back to the palate.

4. Have the child place the end of a long food such as String Thing candy, strips of Fruit Roll-Ups, or cooked spaghetti on the alveolar ridge and hold it in place with the front of his tongue to the count of 10. See if he can maintain the hold as you gently attempt to pull it out.

Direct Techniques to Facilitate Sound Placement

Repeat each technique three times. Review the *Program Sequence*, *Program Guidelines*, and *Illustrated Oral-Motor Techniques* in the introductory pages as needed.

1. Rub the sides and tip of the child's tongue and his alveolar ridge with texture (washcloth, Toothette, toothbrush, Infa-dent, or cotton swab) as you name the points of contact.

2. Use your gloved finger to apply deep pressure to the child's tongue tip and front of his blade with a series of quick taps.

3. Push down on the front of the child's tongue with your gloved finger as the child attempts to push your finger up. Then, push your finger into the child's tongue tip and have the child attempt to push your finger away with his tongue without moving his head.

4. Use your gloved finger to push into the sides of the child's tongue at the front. Push toward the midline as the child pushes against your finger.

5. To get elevation of the tongue sides and tip, stroke forward from the center of the child's tongue to the tip. Do not elicit a gag reflex.

6. Press down on the top of the front of the tongue at the center. Slowly lift your finger and ask the child to follow your finger with his tongue.

7. Hold a sucker, Popsicle, pretzel, carrot stick, celery stick, or tongue depressor vertically in front of the child's mouth. Without moving his head, have the child use his tongue to lick from the bottom to the top of the object. Repeat and provide proprioceptive input by pulling down on the object as the child licks up.

8. Hold a small dental floss holder with floss in it behind the child's front teeth. Have the child tap the floss or sustain touch on the floss with his tongue tip.

9. Put a thin cocktail straw or coffee stirrer laterally behind the child's front teeth. Have him hold it there for a count of 10 using only the front of his tongue. Don't let him close his jaw to hold the straw. You can also place the straw on the central groove of the child's tongue and have him hold it against the alveolar ridge.

Tips and Troubleshooting Techniques

For the child who has difficulty achieving or maintaining tongue elevation:

1. Make the child aware of the physical characteristics of the sound. Use a verbal description or body movements.

2. Use a touch cue like a sustained touch above both sides of the child's upper lip with your index and middle fingers in a V as the child produces the target sound in isolation, syllables, or words. Use hand signals to cue the child to use a tongue-up placement during his productions. (See pages 174-176 in the *Materials Book*).

3. Check the lingual frenum for adequate length for tongue elevation.

4. Make sure the child is using the tip or front of his tongue for contact with the alveolar ridge. Make sure the front of the child's tongue is elevating and isn't coming forward between his teeth.

5. Check the amount of jaw or mouth opening and adjust as needed. For jaw stability, have the child rest his chin in his cupped hands or on his fist as he attempts sound productions. Provide other jaw stability techniques as needed. For jaw grading, have the child bite crackers or carrot or celery sticks prior to speech practice.

6. Concentrate on establishing independent tongue action separate from the jaw. Place a thin object like a cocktail straw or the flat surface of a tongue depressor between the child's molars on one side as a bite block. Have the child elevate his tongue tip to his alveolar ridge as he maintains his bite on the object.

7. If the child needs more tactile and visual cueing to achieve placement for /l/, have him start with his tongue tip on the lower edge of his maxillary teeth and then slide his tongue back to his alveolar ridge maintaining contact. Use a mirror.

8. If the child is rounding his lips (which encourages substitution of /w/), have him smile slightly. You can also encourage lip retraction by stroking his lips from the center to the corners or by having him say words or syllables that contain the vowel /i/ (eee) like *leak*, *leap*, or *believe*.

9. If the child's tongue tip is inverted or retroflexed so it's turned too far back toward the palate, apply more stimulation to the tip and front of the tongue. Increase awareness by rubbing the tongue tip and front with a cotton swab dipped in mouthwash. Then, touch the swab to the points of alveolar contact.

10. If the child's tongue is too broad or is moving forward and fat, use techniques for increasing a central groove. Also, press in on the front sides of the child's tongue, one side at a time, as the child resists.

11. If the child's tongue is flaccid, or there isn't enough tension in his tongue, begin by building muscle tone throughout the body (Whole Body Wake-Ups), then the face (Face Wake-Ups), and then the tongue (Direct Techniques).

12. If the child cannot establish a tongue elevation placement for sound production, use an alternate placement. Have the child place the tip of his tongue down in contact with his lower central incisors with the center toward the alveolar ridge. The sides of his tongue should be in proximity with his upper teeth or alveolar ridge. You might also try an interdental placement temporarily until the child can establish a more mature tongue placement.

13. If the child isn't getting enough air build-up for the sound, or isn't getting a good release, work on respiration and breath support while he is producing the sound.

    ◆ push in on the child's diaphragm

    ◆ have him lie on his stomach on the floor propped on his elbows with his head up and forward, not sunk between his shoulders

    ◆ have him lie over a big ball as you hold him at the hips and push into the ball to bounce him

14. To get voicing, have the child elevate his tongue into position for /l/ and initiate voicing while maintaining the placement. You might also try having the child:

    ◆ start with another voiced sound such as /n/. Have him sustain the /n/, then release his tongue into /l/

    ◆ hum with his tongue elevated, then releasing for /l/

    ◆ go from a vowel to /l/ ("ah-l")

15. If the child can achieve correct tongue positioning, but can't release his tongue for the /l/, use a small dental holder with floss. Place it in the child's mouth at the point of tongue tip contact behind the tongue. As the child says the sound, pull the floss and his tongue forward so the child gets the feeling of release. Use a mirror.

Tracking Sheet for Oral-Motor Stimulation

Name _____

Preparing for Speech for the /l/ sound	Dates			
1. Whole Body Wake-Ups				
a. burst-of-air				
b. resistive sucking				
c. resistive movements				
2. Face Wake-Ups				
a. pat parts of face				
b. lick teeth				
c. lick sticky food off lip				
d. rub gums				
3. Jaw Stability				
a. open/close mouth against resistance				
b. push in on chin				
c. rest chin in hands				
d. chewing/biting foods				
4. Vocal Warm-Ups				
a. isolated vowel productions				
b. vowel sequences				
c. tongue clicks				
d. syllable strings				
5. Taste and Food Activities				
a. _____				
b. _____				
c. _____				
6. Direct Facilitation Techniques				
a. rub tongue tip, sides and alveolar ridge				
b. tap tongue tip and front				
c. push down on tongue front				
d. push into tip and front sides				
e. stroke center of tongue, middle to tip				
f. press top center of tongue and lift finger				
g. lick up object held in front of mouth				
h. touch dental floss				
i. tongue tip holds object on alveolar ridge				
j. other techniques/cues				
_____				
_____				
_____				

Comments:

Activities

Give the child the worksheet and materials necessary to complete each activity. Practice each target sound, syllable, or word three times. Write target syllables or words on the worksheets or glue on word pictures. Provide all the cues the child needs to successfully produce the target sound. Send completed worksheets home for additional practice.

Materials needed for the /l/ worksheets:

- ◆ scissors
- ◆ glue
- ◆ markers
- ◆ crayons
- ◆ pencil

Activities for the /l/ sound

1. On the *Daddy Long Legs* worksheet, cut out the shoes at the bottom of the worksheet. Have the child say the /l/ sound in isolation and then glue a shoe on one of the spider's feet. When there is a shoe on every foot, let the child color the spider.

2. Write /l/ + vowel or vowel + /l/ syllable combinations on the *Looking for Lucky Clovers* worksheet. Have the child say a syllable three times and then color a clover green.

3. Write initial /l/ words on the hurdles on the *Leaping Lizards* worksheet. Have the child say a word on a hurdle three times and then decorate a lizard.

4. Write final /l/ words on the wall on the *Humpty Dumpty* worksheet. Have the child say a word on the wall three times and then color a piece of Humpty. When all the words have been practiced and all the pieces have been colored, have the child draw Humpty sitting on the wall.

5. Write medial /l/ words on the seeds on the bottom of the *Melon Mania* worksheet and cut them out. Have the child choose a seed, say the word on it three times, and then glue the seed on the watermelon. When all the seeds are glued on, let the child color the watermelon.

6. Write multisyllabic /l/ words on the lemons on the *Lemonade Time* worksheet. Have the child say a word on a lemon three times and then color a lemon.

7. On the *The Neighborhood* worksheet, there are many /l/ words pictured in all positions of words for additional practice or for phrase and sentence practice. After the child has identified and practiced the words, have him circle the pictures that have his target sound.

   The following /l/ words are targeted in this scene:

ladder	lawn mower	helmet	pliers
lady	lemonade (stand)	mailbox	police car
lamp	basketball	mail carier	wall
laundry	clothesline	people	tool

Chapter 8
Palatal Glide Sounds /r, er/

How the /r, er/ sounds are made:
The tongue is tensed and retracted with the back lateral margins elevated and in contact with the upper back molars and gums. The front is bunched in a medial or neutral position without specific contact points. The tongue is relatively broad and the teeth are slightly open. The tip of the tongue may be slightly elevated and/or turned back. Because the /r, er/ are movement sounds, the positioning of the tongue is influenced by the preceding or following vowel. The lips are relaxed and also take on the shape of the preceding or following vowel.

Initial /r/ is less influenced by surrounding sounds as the placement is more well established and is held longer than other forms. The airstream is voiced. The tongue may also be in a retroflex position where the tongue tip is up and back. The sides are in close proximity or in contact with the upper molars. The retroflex is a less common position for /r, er/.

There are several variables to achieving a successful /r, er/ production. If the child is unable to achieve or stabilize an /r, er/ production, check each key variable.

- ◆ Is there adequate tongue strength and volitional control?

- ◆ Is there an appropriate amount of tension in the tongue?

- ◆ Is the tongue retracted?

- ◆ Is the tongue tip in a medial position, tensed and bunched? Or, in the retroflex positioning, is the tongue tip elevated and back?

- ◆ Are the back lateral margins of the tongue spread and elevated so that the tongue assumes a spoon-like shape?

- ◆ Does the tongue move independently from the jaw?

- ◆ Is the jaw in a neutral position and stable, without a forward, sliding, or excessive opening during productions?

It's important to recognize that there are six different /r, er/ forms and that they should be taught in a systematic sequence. The different types of the /r, er/ sounds are:

1. unstressed /er/: the sound is within the unstressed syllable in words like *paper, neighbor, tiger*

2. stressed /er/: the sound is within the stressed syllable of the word and makes up the primary vowel heard in the syllable in words like *bird, girl, birthday*

3. vowel-controlled /er/: the sound is preceded by an audible vowel sound in words like *door, tire, car*

4. intervocalic /er/: the sound is between two vowels and both an /er/ and a /r/ sound are heard in words like *carrot, arrow, arrive*

5. initial /r/: the /r/ is the first sound in words like *read, run, roof*

6. /r/ blends: the /r/ follows another consonant sound in words like *brown, tree, drink*

The sequence for teaching /r, er/ is found on pages 108-109.

Preparing for Speech

After you prepare the child's body, face, and speech mechanism for speech practice, provide direct techniques for sound facilitation. Follow this with speech practice. Implement troubleshooting techniques as needed. Don't forget to wear protective gloves when working in or around a child's face or mouth.

Whole Body Wake-Ups

Have the child:

♦ do long, sustained movements such as sliding, swinging, rolling, or pulling.

♦ do resistive movements such as pulling hard on a rope or carrying a heavy chair or basket of toys.

♦ do "Row Your Boat." Sit on the floor across from the child with the soles of your feet against hers. Hold hands to make your boat. Pull on the child so she rocks forward. Have her pull to rock you forward. As you rock back and forth sing "Row, Row, Row Your Boat."

♦ drink a cool tart drink such as lemonade or cranberry juice through a thin straw to facilitate elevation of the back of the tongue.

Face Wake-Ups

1. Have the child pat her cheeks, lips, and under her chin using her index and middle fingers.

2. Use a gloved finger, Infa-dent, Toothette, washcloth, or a Popsicle to rub along the inside upper gum behind the child's teeth from molar to molar three times. Stroke the entire upper surface of the tongue, including the center and sides from the tip to the back. Name the parts you touch to increase the child's awareness.

3. Put your thumb and index finger at each corner of the child's top lip. Stroke from the corners to the center of the lip, then gently grasp and shake the lip. Do the same to the child's lower lip.

4. Have the child yawn and swallow.

Jaw Stability

Gently push downward on the chin as the child attempts to keep her mouth closed (resistance), then push upward while the child attempts to open her mouth.

Provide proprioceptive input by pushing inward on the point of the chin with deep pressure for a few seconds and/or massaging the muscles around the temporal-mandibular joint.

Vocal Warm-Ups

Have the child:

♦ imitate vowels and vowel sequences.

♦ say a sequence of vowels or syllables that use different movements of the tongue (i.e., spreading, retraction, elevation). Good target syllables could include "ee-ee-ee, yuh-yuh-yuh, la-la-la," or "key-key-key."

♦ say silly /r/ sounds such as a rooster crowing, tires squealing, a car crash sound, or growling.

Taste and Food Activities to Facilitate Tongue Elevation, Spreading, and Retraction

1. Have the child chew a piece of cinnamon, peppermint, or spearmint gum to alert the oral area. Have her chew and then hold the gum against the front of her palate with her tongue tip for a few seconds. Then have her chew and hold again. This can also be done with a hot (not sour) candy such as Hot Tamales or War Heads.

2. Have the child hold the end of a strip of food (cooked spaghetti, String Thing candy, Fruit Roll-Up, or a stick of chewing gum) against her alveolar ridge using the tip and front of her tongue for a count of 10. See if she can maintain the hold as you gently attempt to pull the food out. Then have her work the entire length of the food into her mouth, focusing on her tongue without allowing her fingers or lips to help much.

3. Have the child bite crackers or carrot and celery sticks to facilitate jaw grading ability.

4. Place a small amount of a sticky food such as peanut butter, jelly, or marshmallow cream on the center of the child's alveolar ridge and palate. Have the child use the front of her tongue to lick from the alveolar ridge back to the palate. Put some above her upper lip and have her lick it off.

5. Have the child suck a lozenge or mint for tongue spreading.

Direct Techniques for Sound Placement Facilitation

These techniques are listed in a general progression to address the key variables for achieving correct /r, er/ placement and productions. The techniques under each heading may target more than one element, but not all techniques need to be implemented. You'll need to determine which factors are contributing to /r, er/ placement difficulty and which areas need to be addressed. Repeat each technique three times. Review the *Program Sequence, Program Guidelines*, and *Illustrated Oral-Motor Techniques* in the introductory pages as needed.

1. Facilitate jaw stability and graded jaw movements so that jaw positioning is controlled and the tongue moves independently from the jaw. It's important to check jaw positioning and stability carefully. Many children who distort /er/ have difficulty maintaining a neutral jaw position. They may jut their jaw forward, laterally, or use a lax open jaw which can pull the tongue out of position.

    a. Check for 90°-90°-90° sitting with the head in midline and the chin slightly tucked. The child may sit on the floor as long as her back is straight, her head is upright in a midline position, and her chin is slightly tucked. Or, have the child lie on her stomach propped on elbows with her head up and forward, not sunk between her shoulders.

    b. Before speech practice, have the child bite crackers, celery or carrot sticks, or other foods that facilitate jaw grading.

    c. There are several ways to help get the jaw into proper alignment including:

    ◆ applying pressure into the point of the child's chin with your thumb

    ◆ using a bite block between the molars to provide jaw stability during speech production

    ◆ having the child cup her chin in her hands, with the palms on the chin during speech production. (This helps her stabilize the jaw as well as monitor when it moves out of position.) Make sure she keeps her head in midline and straight, not tilted back.

    ◆ having the child lie on her stomach with her chin on her fist or cupped in her palms during speech production

    ◆ using a mirror as needed

2. Facilitate an appropriate amount of tension throughout the tongue.

    a. Place your gloved finger along the entire length of one side of the child's tongue. First push into one side, then the other. Repeat and have the child push against your finger with her tongue (resistance).

b. Using a gloved finger, push down on the entire top of one side of the child's tongue, then the other side. Repeat with the child using her tongue to push up against your finger (resistance).

c. Push down on the center of the front of the child's tongue with your gloved finger as the child attempts to push your finger up (resistance).

d. If the child's tongue is overly tense so the child distorts /er/ to /uh/, work on tongue position (spreading and elevation of the back especially), and a reduction of tension in the tongue. It may help to close the child's jaw a little and have her produce /er/ with a rising pitch. Talk to the child about using easy productions without excessive tension. Monitor lip, jaw, and neck tension.

e. If the child doesn't have enough tension in her tongue, repeat whole body wake-ups, face wake-ups, the direct techniques above, and then those techniques that encourage tongue elevation and spreading. (See #4 below.)

3. Facilitate retraction of the tongue with elevation of the back.

a. Using a gloved finger, Infa-dent, Toothette, washcloth, or cotton swab dipped in mouthwash, stroke the sides of the child's tongue and her upper molars and gums. Then, have the child raise her tongue so its sides are in contact with the sides of her teeth. Have her slowly slide her tongue back, maintaining a contact between the sides of her tongue and her molars.

b. Have the child gently bite the sides of her tongue between her molars and slide her tongue back.

c. Stroke the child's tongue along the central groove from back to front, starting at the middle and moving forward to the tip.

d. Put a tongue depressor into the tip of the child's tongue. Push the child's tongue straight back for the /er/. Or, put the depressor under the front of the child's tongue and push back and slightly up.

e. Touch the back of the child's head at the base of the skull as she retracts her tongue. Or, gently pull the child's hair back at the base of her skull. These techniques give tactile information about tongue retraction.

4. Facilitate elevation of the back and sides of the tongue, and spreading of the tongue.

a. Using a gloved finger, Infa-dent, Toothette, washcloth, or cotton swab dipped in mouthwash, stroke the sides of the child's tongue and her upper molars and gums where contact is made.

b. Place your gloved finger along the entire length of one side of the child's tongue. Push into that side, then the other. Repeat and have the child push against your finger with her tongue (resistance).

   c. Lay your gloved finger on top of the entire length of one side of the child's tongue. Push down on that side, then the other. Repeat and have the child push up against your finger with her tongue (resistance).

   d. Place a Y-shaped dental floss holder with the Y flat between the child's molars, and have the child bite down lightly. Instruct the child to touch both sides of her tongue to the sides of the holder and pull her tongue back. This encourages tongue spreading as well as retraction. You can add floss to the holder to increase tactile input.

   e. Place your index finger under the child's chin at the juncture of her jaw and neck. Press upward on the base of the child's tongue without pushing her head back as she says the /er/ sound.

5. Facilitate a central groove in the midline of the tongue to get a spoon-shaped tongue placement with the back sides elevated.

   a. Encourage a bowling of the tongue and elevation of the sides of the tongue by stroking the center of the child's tongue from the tip to the middle of the tongue with a gloved finger.

   b. Using your finger, apply quick taps with deep pressure along the central groove of the child's tongue from the tip to halfway back.

6. Facilitate elevation of the tongue tip and front.

   a. Place your gloved fingertip against the child's tongue tip and press into it. Repeat and have the child push against your finger with her tongue tip (resistance) without moving her head.

   b. Place your gloved finger on top of the child's tongue tip. Push down on the tongue as the child pushes up (resistance).

   c. Place the tip of a tongue depressor on the child's alveolar ridge and have the child hold it in position using the tip of her tongue.

   d. Use your gloved finger to apply deep pressure to the front of the child's tongue and tongue tip in a series of quick taps.

   e. Use your gloved finger to push into the sides of the child's tongue at the front. Push toward the midline of the tongue as the child pushes against your finger (resistance).

   f. Press down on the front of the center of the child's tongue with your finger. Slowly lift your finger and ask the child to follow it with her tongue.

   g. Put a tongue depressor under or into the tip of the child's tongue. Push the child's tongue back and slightly up for the /er/. For the retroflex position, push the tongue tip up and back.

Tips and Troubleshooting Techniques

For the child who has difficulty achieving or maintaining tongue elevation, spreading, and retraction:

1. Make the child aware of how the sound is produced (gliding sustained sound). Use a verbal description or body movements.

2. Use touch cues to the child's face as she produces the target sound in isolation, syllables, or words. Make a Y-shape using your thumb and middle finger. Place your fingers on either cheek at the level of the upper molars. Use hand signals to cue the child to use appropriate tongue placement during her productions. (See pages 174-176 in the *Materials Book*.)

3. Check the lingual frenum for adequate length for tongue retraction and elevation.

4. Go from another sound production to /er/. You may need to use a tongue depressor to aid in transition of movement from one sound placement to another. A mirror can be helpful.

   a. Encourage tongue spreading by starting with a sound such as *ee* and going to /er/. Then have the child pull her tongue back to the /er/ placement. (*Y*, *zh*, *j*, *sh*, and *th* are also good sounds to begin a syllable with.)

   b. Begin at the back of the mouth by having the child say *k* or *g* (velars) and moving her tongue to /er/.

   c. Begin at the front of the mouth by having the child say *t* or *d* (lingua-alveolars) and moving her tongue back to /er/.

   d. Have the child begin with a mouth-open vowel posture and glide into /er/. Experiment with various vowels followed by /er/ to see if one facilitates placement. The vowels *ee* and *ah* tend to be more facilitating.

   e. Try sequencing sounds where the tongue progressively retracts. For example, have the child slowly glide from *zh* to *y* to *ee* to /er/ to produce "zh-y-ee-er."

   f. For a retroflex position, begin with *l* or *n* and go to /er/.

5. If the child is substituting *w* for /r/, encourage lip spreading rather than rounding.

   a. Have the child use a mirror to monitor lip position.

   b. Stroke the child's lips from the corners to the center and then gently shake the center to reduce lip tension.

   c. Have the child smile and elongate the /r/ sound.

   d. Place two fingers on each side of the child's face and slowly vibrate along each of the facial muscles from the point of origin to the point of insertion at the mouth. A slow vibration will reduce facial tension.

e. Have the child cup her chin with both hands on her cheeks during /r/ practice. This will enable her to feel the difference between spread lips and pursed lips.

6. If the child's lips are overly retracted and tense, rub from the center of the lips out to the corners and then shake them gently. Talk about using an easy or soft smile rather than a wide lip retraction.

Tracking Sheet for Oral-Motor Stimulation

Name _____

Preparing for Speech for the /r, er/ sound	Dates			
1. Whole Body Wake-Ups				
a. sustained movements				
b. resistive movements				
c. "Row Your Boat"				
d. tart drink with thin straw				
2. Face Wake-Ups				
a. face pats				
b. rub molar to molar, tongue				
c. stroke/shake lips				
d. yawn, swallow				
3. Jaw Stability				
a. open/close mouth against resistance				
b. push in on chin				
c. rest chin in hands/on fist				
d. bite block				
4. Vocal Warm-Ups				
a. isolated vowel productions				
b. vowel sequences				
c. say vowel sequences/syllables				
d. silly /r/ sounds: rooster, tire squeal, car crash, growl				
e. other				
5. Taste and Food Activities				
a. _____				
b. _____				
c. _____				
6. Direct Facilitation Techniques				
a. push into sides/front sides of tongue				
b. push down on top of tongue sides/front				
c. stroke sides of tongue, molars, gums				
d. bite tongue sides				
e. tap/stroke tongue center, tip to middle				
f. dental floss holder, tongue spreading & retraction				
g. push into/down on tongue tip				
h. press down on tongue front, lift finger				
i. tongue depressor, push into/under tongue tip				
j. other techniques/cues				
_____				
_____				
_____				

Comments:

Teaching /r/ and /er/

You will need to probe each of the six /r, er/ forms in words to determine stimulability or to determine which production context is easiest for the child. It's important to work in a sequence that progressively practices the /r, er/ in more difficult contexts. By developing a sequential plan, you can easily see where the system breaks down, and can adjust your therapy accordingly. One reason children may have so much difficulty establishing consistent productions for /r, er/ during therapy is the lack of a therapy progression that emphasizes each /r, er/ form separately. The suggested sequence for therapy is as follows:

1. Begin with /er/ placement using oral-motor facilitation techniques. When the child has established placement and can produce the isolated /er/ with accuracy, move to the next step.

2. Introduce the /er/ sound in consonant syllable units. Put a consonant sound in front of the /er/ sound and have the child repeat the syllable after you. You'll need to probe to determine which consonant is most facilitating for the child. Provide practice for all sounds within each placement grouping (i.e., bilabial, labiodental, lingua-alveolar, palatal, velar, etc.) until the child reaches accuracy. (Example: *per, ber, ter, der, ser, zer*) Emphasize the /er/ by elongating it. This gives the child an opportunity to achieve and hold the placement long enough to be successful. See the word lists at the end of this chapter for practice syllables.

3. Introduce unstressed /er/ words incorporating the consonant syllable units practiced above. Select one placement grouping such as bilabial to target initially. Have the child practice the consonant syllable unit several times. (Example: *per, per, per*)

   Then have the child practice unstressed /er/ words containing that same syllable. (Example: *paper, diaper, helper*) Also have the child practice the paired cognate syllables and words. (Example: *ber, ber, ber, number, robber, labor*)

   Break the word as needed to emphasize the consonant syllable unit, elongating the /er/ sound. (Example: *ba-ker, tea-cher, lad-der*) Use more natural productions of the second syllable as the child is ready for them.

   Continue working on unstressed /er/ words within each placement grouping (i.e., bilabial, labiodental, lingua-alveolar, palatal, velar, etc.) until the child can produce them with accuracy following a model. See the word lists at the end of this chapter for practice words.

4. Introduce stressed /er/ words. Some children find these easier to produce than the unstressed /er/. Probe and adjust your therapy plan as needed. Again, start with the consonant /er/ syllable units in placement groupings (as in teaching the unstressed /er/ above). Practice the syllable, then the stressed /er/ words containing that syllable. (Example: *ber, ber, ber, burn, bird, Burt, burst*) Emphasize the stressed /er/ in the word by having the child hold her tongue position and make the sound longer than usual. Have her pause slightly before producing the final consonant or syllable in the word. Errors usually occur when the child moves her tongue too quickly to the following consonant before establishing a good /er/ sound. Blend the word together as the child is ready for it. See the word list at the end of this chapter for practice words.

108

5. Introduce vowel-controlled /er/ words. Begin with one vowel plus /er/, probing to see which vowel facilitates the /er/. Then, practice this vowel plus /er/ syllable in words. (Example: *pair, fair, care, dare*) When the child is successful, introduce a new vowel plus /er/ in syllables and then words. It may be helpful to have the child elongate the vowel before producing the /er/. See the word list at the end of this chapter for practice words.

6. Begin on intervocalic /er-r/. In each word, elongate the vowel plus /er/ in the first syllable and then glide from the /er/ to the /r/ in the second syllable. (Example: *very, story, terrible*) Some children find it easier to work on intervocalic /er-r/ following work on initial /r/ productions. See the word list at the end of this chapter for practice words.

7. Introduce initial /r/ words. Some children may find it easiest to begin with the /er/ production and elongate it to glide to /r/. Begin practice with one-syllable words. Because the vowel following /r/ can affect placement, probe to determine which one facilitates the production. Suggest that the child elongate the production of /r/ to fully establish position before beginning the following sound. See the word list at the end of this chapter for practice words.

8. Initiate work on /r/ blends. Begin with the same consonant syllable units used at the beginning of the therapy sequence, working in placement groupings (i.e., bilabial, labiodental, lingua-alveolar, palatal, velar, etc.). Have the child practice briefly on a consonant syllable unit. Then introduce /r/ blend words that contain that unit. (Example: *ber, ber, bread, broken, brown, break*) Suggest that the child initially elongate the production of /r/ to fully establish position before beginning the following sound so he has an intervocalic production of /er, r/. Some children are more successful targeting blends before targeting initial /r/. There is no word list for blends as this program does not address blend productions.

Activities

Give the child the worksheet and materials necessary to complete the activity. Practice each target sound, syllable, or word three times. Write target syllables or words on the worksheets or glue on word pictures. Provide all the cues the child needs to successfully produce the target sound. Send completed worksheets home for additional practice.

The activity pages are in the same sequence as suggested for teaching /r, er/:

- isolation
- consonant plus /er/ syllable units
- unstressed /er/ words
- stressed /er/ words
- vowel-controlled /er/ words
- intervocalic /er/ words
- initial /r/ words

Because the /r, er/ sound is difficult to establish in all contexts, two worksheets are included for each sound type.

Materials needed for the /r, er/ worksheets:

- markers
- crayons
- pencil
- scissors
- glue

Activities for the /r, er/ sounds

1. On the *Rowdy Roosters* worksheet, have the child say the /er/ sound in isolation three times and then color a rooster.

2. On the *Something's In There* worksheet, cut out the animals at the bottom of the page and write /er/ on each one. Have the child say the /er/ sound three times in isolation and then glue an animal in the cave. When all the animals are in the cave, have the child color them.

3. On *The Syllable Rap* worksheet, write a consonant before each /er/. Have the child say a syllable three times and then color a musical note.

4. On *The Purr-fect Meal* worksheet, cut out the cat tails at the bottom of the page and write a consonant plus /er/ syllable on each one. Have the child say a syllable three times and then glue a tail on one of the cats. When all of the cats have tails, have the child color them.

110

5. Write words with unstressed /er/ on the top of the suitcase on the *See You Later, Alligator* worksheet. Have the child say a word three times and then draw something in Walter's suitcase. When his suitcase is full, have the child color the alligator green.

6. Write words with an unstressed /er/ on *The Collector* worksheet. Have the child say a word three times and then draw a rung on the ladder.

7. Write words with stressed /er/ on Burt's shirt on the *Rehearse the Verse* worksheet. Have the child practice each word three times and then check it off on Burt's shirt. Write that word in the verse that Burt is holding. When the verse is finished, read it aloud with the child saying the stressed /er/ words.

8. Write words with stressed /er/ on the turtle shells on the *Turtle Hatching Time* worksheet. Have the child practice a word on a turtle three times and then color the turtle's shell.

9. Write vowel-controlled /er/ words on the *Telling Stories* worksheet. Have the child say a word three times and then draw a marshmallow on one of the animal's sticks.

10. Write vowel-controlled /er/ words on the *Board by Board* worksheet. Have the child say a word three times and then color a board on the fence.

11. Write intervocalic /er/ words on the bucket on the *Berry Picking Time* worksheet. Have the child say a word on the bucket three times and then draw a strawberry in the basket.

12. Write intervocalic /er/ words on the *Harry's Corral* worksheet. Have the child say a word three times and then draw a lasso around the neck of one of the horses.

13. Write initial /r/ words on the *Rings Around Rosie* worksheet. Have the child say a word three times and then color a ring around Rosie.

14. Write initial /r/ words on the *Rolling Along* worksheet. Have the child say a word three times and then color a cactus.

15. On the *Volunteers at Work* worksheet, there are many /r/ words pictured in all positions of words for additional practice or phrase and sentence practice. After the child has identified and practiced the /r/ words, have her circle the pictures with the /r/ sound.

    The following /r/ words are targeted in this scene:

initial	stressed /er/	unstressed /er/	vowel-controlled /er/	intervocalic /er/
radio	circle	carpenter	board	garage
roof	curb	hammer	car	wheelbarrow
room	dirt	ladder	door	
	work	lumber	stairs	
		number	volunteer	
		painter		

Word List for /r, er/ Productions

Consonant Syllable Units (C + /er/)

bilabial: ber/burr, per/purr, mer, wer/were
labiodental: fer/fur, ver
lingua-alveolar: der, ter, ner
velar: ker/curr, ger/grr, her
lingua-alveolar strident: ser/sir, zer
palatal: sher/sure, cher, jer
lingua-alveolar glide: ler
linguadental: ther

Unstressed /er/ words

bilabial

per	ber	mer	wer
slipper	number	summer	tower
diaper	neighbor	plumber	flower
temper	remember	timer	sour
helper	robber	hammer	hour
deeper	lumber	Homer	our
whisper	September	simmer	shower
zipper	October	climber	power
supper	November	farmer	lower
paper	timber	swimmer	mower
hamper	member	calmer	flour

labiodental

fer	ver
offer	over
Jennifer	fever
prefer	never
transfer	diver
wafer	mover
loafer	cover
roofer	clover
tougher	liver
golfer	river
safer	whatever

lingua-alveolar

ter	der	ner
winter	under	dinner
actor	powder	runner
after	ladder	banner
later	leader	can opener
better	shoulder	finer
water	calendar	cleaner
butter	colder	winner
center	thunder	spinner
letter	fender	strainer
painter	louder	miner

velar

ker	ger
baker	tiger
sucker	finger
hiker	longer
locker	bigger
banker	eager
walker	sugar
anchor	anger
soccer	digger
biker	hunger
acre	vigor

lingua-alveolar strident

ser	zer
saucer	laser
looser	fertilizer
dancer	loser
boxer	visor
mixer	razor
answer	buzzer
nicer	wiser
closer	chooser
officer	
eraser	

palatal

sher	**cher**	**jer**
washer	teacher	danger
usher	lecture	ginger
gusher	adventure	soldier
wisher	pitcher	messenger
glacier	catcher	passenger
pressure	butcher	badger
	nature	Roger
	future	manager
	bleacher	injure
	creature	major

lingua-alveolar glide

ler
sailor
solar
peeler
tailor
collar
dollar
color
taller
molar
smaller

linguadental

ther
panther
mother
father
brother
bother
lather
weather
feather
gather
other

Stressed /er/ words

bilabial

per	**ber**	**mer**	**wer**
person	burp	mermaid	word
perfect	burst	mercy	worst
perch	burden	mirth	world
purple	auburn	merchant	worm
purse	birthday	mercury	worth
pearl	bird	Merlin	work
purchase	burn	merge	worse
purpose	Burt	merchandise	coward
leopard	bluebird	murky	toward
shepherd	iceberg		upward

labiodental

fer	**ver**
fur/fir	verb
first	verse
firm	vertical
fern	verdict
first aid	convert
comfort	government
furnish	verge
furnace	Vernon
different	Vern
Clifford	vermin

lingua-alveolar

ter	**der**	**ner**
turn	dirt	nurse
turkey	derby	nerve
turf	dirty	nourish
turtle	wonderful	Nerf®
term	standard	energy
turquoise	wilderness	nursing
termite	Dirk	nervous
attorney		
western		
pattern		

velar

ker	ger	her
curb	girl	hurt
curve	Gertrude	her
cursive	Gert	herself
curtain	gurney	hurl
curfew	girth	hurdle
current		Herman
curl		Hershey®
kernel		Herb
Curtis		herd/heard

lingua-alveolar strident

ser	zer
sir	lizard
circle	wizard
certain	dessert
sermon	desert
search	buzzard
surf	berserk
circus	
serve	
surface	
serpent	

palatal

sher	cher	jer
shirt	chirp	jerk
sure	church	germ
Shirley	churn	German
Sherman	churning	Germany
sherbet		gerbil
shirk		jersey
shirttail		New Jersey
		geranium
		journal
		journey

lingua-alveolar glide

ler
learn
lurch
lurk
alert

linguadental

ther
third
thirst
thirsty
thirty
Thursday
thirteen
thermometer
thermos

Vowel-controlled /er/ words

long vowels

a	e	i	o	u
air	ear	dryer	bore	cure
bear	dear	buyer	core	manure
care	fear	wire	four/for	lure
fair	hear	liar	more	tour
hair	near	fire	pour	sewer
chair	cheer	tire	roar	
where	gear	higher	sore	
tear	jeer	crier	tore	
pear	peer	dire	or	
share	rear	hire	wore	

short vowel

a	
arm	harm
barn	are
charm	art
far	heart
car	arch

Intervocalic /er-r/ words

around	Cheerios®	hurry	sparrow
arrow	cherry	Jerry	story
berry	current	Larry	surround
borrow	dairy	marry	terrible
burro	fairy	merry	terror
bury	ferry	narrow	Terry
carrot	furry	parrot	tomorrow
carry	giraffe	sheriff	very
celery	hairy	sorry	wary

Initial /r/ words

rabbit	rafter	ranch	rib	roast
raccoon	rag	ran	rice	robe
race	raid	range	ride	roll
racer	rail	rap	ridge	roof
rack	railroad	rapid	right	rope
racket	rain	raw	ripe	rose
radar	rainbow	reach	rise	rude
radio	raincoat	read	roach	run
radish	raisin	real	road	rush
raft	rake	rhyme	roam	wrote

Chapter 9
Linguadental Sound /th/

How the /th/ sounds are made:
There are two /th/ sounds, voiced and unvoiced. For both productions, the tongue tip is wide and flattened with a small central opening. The tongue tip is protruded and placed lightly between the edges of the upper and lower teeth. The main body of the tongue is flat and fills the space between the upper and lower side teeth. The lips are relaxed and slightly parted. The breath is continuous for both productions with the vocal folds vibrating for the voiced /th/.

Preparing for Speech

After you prepare the child's body, face, and speech mechanism for speech practice, provide direct techniques for sound facilitation. Follow this with speech practice. Implement troubleshooting techniques as needed. Don't forget to wear protective gloves when working in or around a child's face and mouth.

Whole Body Wake-Ups

Have the child:

◆ do long, sustained movements such as sliding, swinging, or pulling or do extension activities such as sliding on the stomach, stretching, or lying straight and rolling on a mat.

◆ do blowing activities.

◆ do activities that facilitate respiration/breath support for speech. Have the child take a deep breath as he raises his arms over his head, then blow the air out in a long, easy expiration as he lowers his arms to his sides. Or, have him lie over a big therapy ball or bolster and help him roll forward to touch his hands to the floor, then back to the starting position.

◆ wiggle or crawl on his stomach like a snake. Have him protrude and retract his tongue to make a "snake face."

Face Wake-Ups

1. Have the child pat his cheeks, lips, and under his chin using his index and middle fingers.

2. Stroke the child's top lip from the corners to the center. Then, shake gently. Do the same for the lower lip.

3. Have the child lick the bottom edges of his upper teeth and the top edges of his lower teeth.

4. Hold a Popsicle, spoon coated with peanut butter (or other sticky food), tongue depressor, or flat sucker in front of the child's mouth. Have him protrude his tongue and lick the object without moving his head.

5. Have the child protrude and retract his tongue several times in a row to make "snake faces."

Jaw Stability

Gently push downward on the child's chin as he attempts to keep his mouth closed. Then, push upward while the child attempts to open his mouth. You could also attempt to close the child's mouth when it is open.

Provide proprioceptive input by pushing inward on the point of the chin with deep pressure for a few seconds and/or massaging the muscles around the temporal-mandibular joint.

Vocal Warm-Ups

Have the child:

- ◆ imitate vowels and vowel sequences.

- ◆ make motor boat or "raspberry" sounds with the tongue protruded.

- ◆ sustain a production of /h/ or sigh with sustained airflow.

Taste and Food Activities to Facilitate Tongue Protrusion

1. To facilitate jaw grading, have the child bite crackers, carrot sticks, or celery sticks.

2. Have the child chew cinnamon or peppermint gum and blow bubbles.

3. Have the child suck a lozenge or mint to encourage tongue spreading.

4. Put peanut butter or another sticky food on the child's upper lip and have the child lick it off with his tongue. Do the same on the child's upper central incisors.

5. Have the child lap water out of a cup using his tongue without any head movements.

Direct Techniques to Facilitate Sound Placement

Repeat each technique three times. Review the *Program Sequence*, *Program Guidelines*, and *Illustrated Oral-Motor Techniques* in the introductory pages as needed.

1. Using your finger, an Infa-dent, Toothette, washcloth, or cotton swab dipped in mouthwash, stroke the front and sides of the top of the child's tongue, and the edges of the child's upper and lower teeth. Name the parts as you stroke them.

2. Lay your finger alongside the entire length of one side of the child's tongue. Push into first one side, then the other. Repeat and have the child push against your finger with his tongue (resistance).

3. Using your finger, push down on the top of one side of the child's tongue and then on the other side. Repeat with the child using his tongue to push against your finger.

4. Using your finger, press into the tip of the child's tongue. Repeat, but have the child push back with his tongue without moving his head.

5. Lay your finger on the child's tongue tip and press down. Repeat, but have the child push back with his tongue without moving his head.

6. Using your finger, press in one side of the child's tongue tip, then the other. Repeat with the child pushing into your finger with his tongue.

7. Using your finger, press into the child's tongue tip in his mouth. Slowly pull your finger out of his mouth while instructing the child to maintain tongue contact with your finger. When his tongue is protruded, have him bite gently on his tongue. You may use a tongue depressor instead of your finger.

8. Encourage a bowling of the tongue and a central aperture by stroking the center of the child's tongue from the tip to the middle.

9. Place a bite block between the child's molars to provide jaw stability during speech production. Check for 90°-90°-90° seating with the child's head in midline and his chin slightly tucked. It is also acceptable to have the child lie on his stomach, propped on his elbows with his head up and forward, not sunk between his shoulders.

10. To get proper lip tension and spreading, have the child smile slightly. If the child has too much tension or rounding, stroke each of the child's lips from the corners to the center and shake out gently. To encourage retraction, stroke each of the child's lips from the center to the corners and hold briefly.

Tips and Troubleshooting Techniques

For the child who has difficulty achieving or maintaining tongue protrusion:

1. Make the child aware of the physical characteristics of the sound (long sustained sound). Use a verbal description or body movements.

2. Use touch cues to the child's face as he produces the target sound in isolation, syllables, or words by lightly touching the protruded tongue tip. Use hand signals to cue the child to use appropriate tongue placement during his productions. (See pages 174-176 in the *Materials Book*.)

3. Have the child scrape the front and sides of his tongue against his upper teeth to increase awareness.

4. To direct the airstream and to facilitate a central groove of the tongue, place a straw on the center of the child's tongue. Be sure to only place the straw halfway back or you may gag the child. Have the child hold the straw using his tongue and blow air. Slowly pull the straw out of his mouth while the child follows the straw with his tongue and continues to blow air. Briefly leave the straw on the tip of the tongue. Repeat but decrease the amount of straw in the child's mouth each time until the child is cued simply by having the straw outside his lips.

5. Place a standard size Y-shaped dental floss holder with no floss in the child's mouth, between his molars. Have the child bite down slightly and spread his tongue so the sides of his tongue touch the sides of the holder. Have him put the front of his tongue on the front of the holder. Pull the holder from the child's mouth until the child's tongue protrudes.

6. Hold a straw, tongue depressor, or your finger perpendicular in front of the child's mouth. Have him protrude his tongue to touch the object and then blow air to produce the /th/ sound.

7. Have the child stick out his tongue and bite on it. Use a mirror. Then, have him open his jaw slightly and blow out air for the /th/.

8. Have the child stick out his tongue out as far as possible. Use a mirror. Have him slowly retract his tongue as he blows out air until his tongue is between his front teeth. Then, have him hold the /th/ placement for a few seconds.

9. Start with another sound placement such as /s/ and go to /th/ (to get the fricative and airflow). Or start with "eee" to get tongue spreading and go to /th/.

10. If the child's tongue tip is too fat, increase tension by pushing into the sides of the tongue front. Repeat and have the child push back with his tongue (resistance).

11. If the sound is lateralized, work on the central groove of the tongue.

12. If there is too much tension in the child's lips, relax them by slowly vibrating around and on the lips (obicularis oris muscle) with your fingers. Or, do "bunny noses" by putting your index finger and middle finger on either side of the child's nose. Slowly vibrate down to the upper lip and hold briefly.

Tracking Sheet for Oral-Motor Stimulation

Name _____

Preparing for Speech for the /th/ sound	Dates			
1. Whole Body Wake-Ups				
a. sustained movement				
b. extension activities				
c. blowing				
d. respiration/breath support				
e. crawl on belly				
2. Face Wake-Ups				
a. pat parts of face				
b. stroke/shake lips				
c. lick teeth				
d. lick object/food				
e. protrude/retract tongue				
3. Jaw Stability				
a. open/close mouth against resistance				
b. push in on chin				
c. bite block				
4. Vocal Warm-Ups				
a. isolated vowel productions				
b. vowel sequences				
c. funny sounds: motor boat, raspberries				
d. sustained /h/, sigh				
5. Taste and Food Activities				
a. _____				
b. _____				
c. _____				
6. Direct Facilitation Techniques				
a. stroke front/sides of tongue, edges of teeth				
b. push into sides of tongue and tip				
c. push down on top of sides of tongue				
d. press into/down on front of tongue tip				
e. stroke central groove of tongue				
f. press into tongue tip and pull out finger				
g. smile, stroke, hold/shake lips				
h. other techniques/cues				
_____				
_____				
_____				

Comments:

Activities

Give the child the worksheet and materials necessary to complete the activity. Practice each target sound, syllable, or word three times. Write target syllables or words on the worksheet or glue on word pictures. Provide all the cues the child needs to successfully produce the target sound. Send the completed worksheets home for additional practice.

Materials needed for the /th/ worksheets:

- ◆ markers
- ◆ crayons
- ◆ pencil
- ◆ scissors
- ◆ glue

Activities for the /th/ sound

1. On the *Thea's Birthday Salute* worksheet, have the child say the /th/ sound in isolation. Then, have the child draw a party horn blown straight out.

2. Write /th/ + vowel or vowel + /th/ syllable combinations on the stamps on the *Theodore's Giant Task* worksheet. Have the child say a syllable three times and then draw stamps on the envelopes.

3. Cut out the caps on the bottom of the *Thinking Caps* worksheet. Write initial /th/ words on the caps. Have the child say a word on a cap three times and then glue it on a student's head.

4. Write final /th/ words on the pieces of dried fruit on the *Sweet Tooth* worksheet. Have the child say a word on a piece of fruit three times and then color it.

5. Write medial /th/ words on the apple basket on the *What a Mouthful!* worksheet. Have the child say a word on the basket three times and then draw an apple in the hippo's mouth.

6. Write multisyllabic words on the runners' shirts on the *A Marathon Finish* worksheet. Have the child say a word on a shirt three times and then color the shirt.

7. On the *Family Reunion worksheet*, there are many /th/ words pictured in all positions of words for additional practice or for phrase and sentence practice. After the child has identified and practiced the words, have him circle the pictures that have his target sound.

   The following /th/ words are targeted in this scene:

Theodore	thirty	grandfather	Ruth
thick	birdbath	grandmother	Seth
thin	brother	Kathy	Smith
thirsty	father	mother	tablecloth
thirteenth	feather	mouth	tooth

References

Alexander, R. "Oral-Motor Treatment for Infants and Young Children with Cerebral Palsy." In E. D. Mysak (ed.). *Seminars in Speech and Language.* New York City: Thieme Medical Publishers, Inc., 1987.

Asher, I. E. "Management of Neurologic Disorders—The First Feeding Session." In M. E. Groher (ed.). *Dysphagia: Diagnosis and Management.* Boston: Butterworth, 1984.

Ayres, A. J. *Sensory Integration and the Child.* Los Angeles: Western Psychological Services, 1985.

Bernthal, J. E. and Bankson, N. W. *Articulation Disorders.* Englewood Cliffs, NJ: Prentice Hall, 1981.

Blanche, E. I., Botticelli, T. M., and Hallway, M. K. *Combining Neurodevelopmental Treatment and Sensory Integration Principles.* Tucson, AZ: Therapy Skill Builders, 1995.

Brown, J. C. "Techniques for Correcting /r/ Misarticulations." *Language, Speech, and Hearing Services in Schools*, Vol. VI, No. 2, 1975, pp. 86-91.

Creaghead, N. A., Newman, P. W., and Secord, W. A. *Assessment and Remediation of Articulatory and Phonological Disorders.* Columbus, OH: Merrill Publishing Company, 1985.

DeFazio, J. L. *Intervention in Oral Motor Skills.* Akron, OH: Children's Hospital Medical Center, 1986.

Farber, S. *Neurorehabilitation: A Multisensory Approach.* Philadelphia: W. B. Saunders Co., 1982.

Fink, B. E. *Sensory-Motor Integration Activities.* Tucson, AZ: Therapy Skill Builders, 1989.

Hanson, M. L. and Barrett, R. H. *Fundamentals of Orofacial Myology.* Springfield, IL: Thomas Publishing, 1988.

Hilton, L. M. "Treatment of Deviant Phonological Systems: Tongue Thrust". In W. H. Perkins (ed.). *Phonologic-Articulatory Disorders.* New York City: Thieme-Stratton, Inc., 1983.

Langley, M. B. and Lombardino, L. J. (eds.). *Neurodevelopmental Strategies for Managing Communication Disorders in Children with Severe Motor Dysfunction.* Austin, TX: Pro-Ed, 1991.

Lass, N. J., McReynolds, L. V., Northern, J. l., and Yoder, D. E. *Handbook of Speech-Language Pathology and Audiology.* Toronto: B. C. Decker, Inc., 1988.

Mackie, E. *Oral-Motor Activities for Young Children.* East Moline, IL: LinguiSystems, Inc., 1996.

Marshalla, P. R. "The Role of Reflexes in Oral-Motor Learning: Techniques for Improved Articulation." *Seminars in Speech and Language.* New York City: Thieme, Inc., 1985.

Marshalla, P. R. *Oral-Motor Techniques in Articulation Therapy.* Two-Day Workshop. Cincinnati, OH, April, 1994.

Mason, R. M. and Grandstaff, H. L. "A Method for Eliciting /er/ in Articulation Therapy." *Journal of Tennessee Speech and Hearing Association.* Vol. 17, No. 2, 1970.

Milloy, N. R. *Breakdown of Speech.* London: Chapman and Hall, 1991.

Morris, S. E. "Development of Oral-Motor Skills in the Neurologically-Impaired Child Receiving Non-Oral Feedings." *Dysphagia.* Springer-Verlag. Vol. 3, 1989.

Morris, S. E. and Klein, M. D. *Pre-Feeding Skills*. Tucson, AZ: Therapy Skill Builders, 1987.

Nemoy, E. M. and Davis, S. F. *Correction of Defective Consonant Sounds*. Magnolia, MA: Expression Company, 1969.

New Visions. *Mealtimes*. Rt. 1, Box 175-S, Faber, VA 22938, 1-804-361-2285.

Oetter, P. A. and Laurel, M. *Integration of Speech/Language and Sensorimotor Therapies*. Two-Day Workshop. Cincinnati, OH, April, 1988.

Oetter, P. A., Richter, E. W., and Frick, S. M. *M. O. R. E. Integrating the Mouth with Sensory and Postural Functions*. Hugh, MN: PDP Press, 1995.

Ruscello, D. M. "A Motor Skill Learning Treatment Program for Sound System Disorders." *Seminars in Speech and Language*. New York City: Thieme, Inc., Vol. 14, No. 2, 1993.

Ruscello, D. M. "Motor Learning as a Model for Articulation Instruction." In J. M. Costello (ed.). *Speech Disorders in Children*. San Diego: College Hill Press, 1984.

Shriberg, L. D. "An Intervention Procedure for Children with Persistent /r/ Errors." *Language, Speech, and Hearing Services in Schools*, Vol XI, No. 2, 1980.

Secord, W. *Eliciting Sounds: Techniques for Clinicians*. Columbus, OH: Charles E. Merrill Publishing Co., 1981.

Slipakoff, E. L. "An Approach to the Correction of the Defective /r/." *Journal of Speech and Hearing Disorders*, Vol. XXXII, No. 1, 1967.

Strode, R. M. and Chamberlain, C. E. *Easy Does It for Apraxia and Motor Planning*. East Moline, IL: LinguiSystems, Inc., 1993.

Vaughn, G. R. and Clark, R. M. *Speech Facilitation: Extraoral and Intraoral Stimulation Techniques for Improvement of Articulation Skills*. Springfield, IL: Charles C. Thomas, 1979.

Wilbarger, P. and Wilbarger, J. *Sensory Defensiveness in Children Aged 2-12: An Intervention Guide*. Santa Barbara, CA: Avanti Educational Programs, 1991.

Williams, M. S., and Shellenberger, S. *How Does Your Engine Run? The Alert Program for Self-Regulation*. Albuquerque, NM: Therapy Works, Inc., 1996.

Young, E. H. and Hawk, S. S. *Moto-Kinesthetic Speech Training*. Stanford, CA: Stanford University Press, 1955.

Zemlin, W. R. *Speech and Hearing Science*. Englewood Cliffs, NJ: Prentice Hall, 1988.

Ready for Christmas

Every recipe you need for the holidays from spiking the egg nog to stuffing the goose!

Mary MacPherson
Nancy Davies

Summerhill Press Ltd.
Toronto

© 1986 Mary MacPherson

Published by Summerhill Press Ltd.
Toronto, Ontario

Canadian Cataloguing in Publication Data

MacPherson, Mary
  Ready for Christmas

ISBN 0-920197-32-9

1. Christmas cookery. I. Davies, Nancy, 1946- II. Title.
TX739.M33 1986   641.5'68   C86-094388-7

Distributed in Canada by:
Collier Macmillan Canada
50 Gervais Drive
Don Mills, Ontario M3C 3K4

Cover Photography by Dieter Hessel

Inside Photography:
  Dieter Hessel
  The Borden Company, Limited

Printed and bound in Canada

Cover Props (Poinsettia Pattern) provided by Royal Doulton
Canada Inc.

This book is dedicated with appreciation to friends and relatives who contributed their favourite recipes, and to Mom and Dad, Don, Bill and Harry

Just a Little Foreword

It seems no one is ever "ready for Christmas", especially me! This book was conceived exactly for that purpose – to help you "get ready for Christmas."

For most women, and hopefully me too, Christmas requires a great deal of preparation, a good proportion of which takes place in the kitchen. It is preparation that is both costly in time and in ingredients. Ready for Christmas is a time saver in itself, in so much as every recipe you require is under one cover.

The recipes have been favourites of friends and family over many Christmases and other occasions too.

I would especially like to thank my mother, Margaret MacPherson, who contributed not only her recipes, but often many of her ingredients!

May all your holidays be entertaining ones.

Mary MacPherson

CONTENTS

READY FOR CHRISTMAS

SUMMER BEFORE CHRISTMAS
Begin rum pot.
Make Christmas pudding for best aging.

NOVEMBER 5–11
Buy baking ingredients to save time and money.
Last chance to make Christmas pudding.
Bake Christmas cake for best aging.
Make mincemeat for best aging.

NOVEMBER 12–18
Buy frozen Christmas turkey for the freezer.
Plan Christmas menus.

NOVEMBER 19–25
Make edible gifts for Christmas gift giving.

NOVEMBER 26–DECEMBER 2
Special order fresh Christmas goose, game or turkey.
Make and freeze baked goods.
Make and freeze hors d'oeuvres.
Send Christmas party invitations.

DECEMBER 3–9
Moisten Christmas cake with liquor.
Make and freeze pie shells.
Stock up on canned and frozen foods.
Stock up on non-perishables like crackers, chips, nuts, etc.

DECEMBER 10–16
Last chance to bake Christmas cake.
Stock up on beverages (alcohol, non-alcohol, mix).

DECEMBER 17–24
Glaze Christmas cake.
Freeze extra bags of ice.
Thaw frozen turkey.

DECEMBER 25
Dress turkey.

The Season's Greetings

MULLED CIDER

1 cup	apple cider	250 mL
1	clove	
1	cinnamon stick	

In a saucepan, heat all ingredients. DO NOT BOIL. Serve hot. 1 serving.

HOT CRANBERRY DRINK

1 cup	cranberry juice	250 mL
2	slices lemon	
1	clove	
1	nutmeg, quartered	
	honey to taste	
1	cinnamon stick	

In a saucepan, heat cranberry juice, lemon slices, clove and nutmeg. DO NOT BOIL. Remove clove and add honey to taste. Serve hot with cinnamon stick stirrer. 1 serving.

"At Christmas play and make good cheer,
For Christmas comes but once a year."
Thomas Tusser, **Hundreth Good Pointes Of Husbandrie**

CRANBERRY PERK

2 1/2 cups	water	625 mL
1 cup	cranberry sauce	250 mL
1 cup	pineapple juice	250 mL
1/4 cup	brown sugar	50 mL
1 tbsp	butter	15 mL
pinch	salt, nutmeg, cinnamon, allspice	
4	whole cloves	

In the bottom part of a coffee perculator, place the first 5 ingredients. Wrap the salt and spices in cheesecloth and place in the perculator basket. Perculate through 1 cycle. Serve hot. 6 servings.

HOT BUTTERED CRANBERRY PUNCH

2/3 cup	brown sugar	175 mL
4 cups	water	1 L
1/4 tsp	salt	1 mL
1/4 tsp	nutmeg	1 mL
1/2 tsp	cinnamon	2 mL
1/2 tsp	allspice	2 mL
3/4 tsp	cloves	3 mL
2-15 oz	cans cranberry jelly	2-426 mL
4 cups	unsweetened pineapple juice	1 L
1/2 cup	butter, softened	125 mL
	cinnamon sticks	

In a large saucepan, combine sugar, 1 cup (250 mL) water, salt, and spices and bring to a boil. In a bowl, mix jelly, juice, and remaining water until smooth. Add to saucepan and simmer 10 minutes. Stir in butter. Serve hot with cinnamon stick stirrers. 12 servings.

"Whether they call it Yuletide, Noel, Weinachten, or Christmas, people around the earth thirst for its refreshment as the desert traveller for the oasis."
  D.D. Monroe, Rotarian

HOT TODDY

1/2 tsp	honey	2 mL
1	cinnamon stick	
1-2 oz	brandy, rum, or whiskey	25-30 mL
	boiling water	
	lemon slices	
	cloves	

In a mug, combine honey, cinnamon, and brandy. Fill mug with boiling water. Garnish with lemon slices studded with 2-3 cloves. Serve hot. 1 serving.

HOT BUTTERED RUM

1 tsp	icing sugar	5 mL
1/4 cup	boiling water	50 mL
1/4 cup	rum	50 mL
1 tbsp	butter	15 mL
	boiling water	
	nutmeg, grated	

In a mug, combine icing sugar, 1/4 cup (50 mL) boiling water, rum and butter. Fill mug with boiling water. Garnish with nutmeg. Serve hot. 1 serving

GROG

1/2 tsp	honey	2 mL
1 tsp	ReaLemon lemon juice from concentrate	5 mL
1-2 oz	dark rum	25-50 mL
	boiling water	
	lemon slices	
	nutmeg, grated	

In a mug, combine honey, lemon juice, and rum. Fill mug with boiling water. Garnish with lemon slices and nutmeg. Serve hot or cold. 1 serving.

"Auntie Hannah laced her tea with rum, because it was only once a year."
Dylan Thomas, **Conversation About Christmas**

TOM AND JERRY

1	egg, separated	
1 tsp	sugar	5 mL
1/2 tsp	allspice	2 mL
1 oz	rum	30 mL
1/2 oz	brandy	15 mL
	hot milk (cream)	
	nutmeg, grated	

In a bowl, beat egg yolk and sugar. Add allspice and rum. In a separate bowl, beat egg white until it forms stiff peaks. Fold egg white into egg yolk mixture. Place in mug and add brandy. Fill mug with hot milk and sprinkle with nutmeg. Serve hot. 1 serving.

"I had a stocking this year, full of sweets and cigars and mouth-organs and cherry brandy."
Dylan Thomas, **Letters To Vernon Watkins**

HOT SCOTCH

1	lemon rind and juice	
1/4 cup	sugar	50 mL
6	cloves	
4 cups	water	1 L
3 cups	Scotch whiskey	750 mL

Grate rind of lemon and squeeze juice. Place in a saucepan with sugar, cloves, and water. Bring to a boil. Reduce heat and simmer 3 minutes. Add Scotch and continue heating. DO NOT BOIL. Serve hot. Makes about 1 1/2 qts (1.5 L).

"Too much of anything is bad, but too much whiskey is just enough."
Mark Twain.

HOT 'N' SPICY PUNCH

4 cups	cranberry juice	1 L
3/4 cup	ReaLemon lemon juice from concentrate	175 mL
3/4 cup	brown sugar, firmly packed	175 mL
2 tbsp	honey	30 mL
6	whole cloves	
2	cinnamon sticks	
1 cup	red wine, dry	250 mL
	cinnamon sticks	

In a large saucepan, combine all ingredients except wine. Simmer 10 to 15 minutes. Just before serving, add wine and remove spices. Serve hot with cinnamon stick stirrers. Makes about 1 1/2 qts (1.5 L).

ENGLISH WASSAIL

8	crab apples (6 small apples)	
1 qt	ale	1 L
1 tsp	cinnamon	5 mL
1 tsp	ginger	5 mL
2 cups	sherry	500 mL
1	lemon rind and juice	
	sugar to taste	
2	slices toast, cubed	

Core apples and bake for 20 minutes, or until soft, in a baking dish, at 350 F (180 C). In a large saucepan, bring ale almost to a boil. Stir in spices, sherry, lemon and sugar. Heat until sugar dissolves. Cover and keep on low heat for 30 minutes. DO NOT BOIL. Serve in a punch bowl. Float toast cubes and apples on top. Makes about 1 1/2 qts (1.5 L).

Originally, wassail was taken from one cup, passed in the spirit of friendship (wes hal, 'good health'). Those who couldn't afford to make their own wassail would go a' wassailing--singing carols door to door, carrying an empty wood cup, in hope of receiving some ale.

MULLED WINE

2 1/2 cups	sugar	625 mL
1 1/4 cups	water	300 mL
48	whole cloves	
6	cinnamon sticks	
3	whole nutmegs, crushed	
3	lemons, peel only	
2	oranges, peel only	
4 cups	ReaLemon lemon juice from concentrate, warmed	1 L
4 bottles	red wine	4-750 mL
	lemon slices	

In a large saucepan, boil sugar, water, spices, lemon peel and orange peel for five minutes. Strain liquid and place back in saucepan with warmed lemon juice. Continue to heat and add wine. Garnish with lemon slices. Serve hot. Makes about 6 qts (6 L).

RED SANGRIA

3/4 cup	sugar	175 mL
3/4 cup	unsweetened orange juice, chilled	175 mL
1/3 cup	ReaLemon lemon juice from concentrate	75 mL
1/3 cup	ReaLime lime juice from concentrate	75 mL
6 cups	red wine, medium-dry, chilled	1.5 L
1	orange, sliced	
	ice	

In a tall pitcher, combine sugar and juices. Stir until sugar dissolves. Add wine and orange. Stir to blend. Serve cold over ice. Makes about 2 qts (2 L).

"First, claret for the holiday dinners. Even the children would have a few drops of claret in their glasses—enough to make us feel regal. Then brandy, to put around the pudding and set alight. And sherry, to serve to callers and to put in the grownups' pudding sauce. Children had lemon sauce, but at about twelve years it was possible to graduate to a small helping of the grownups nectar, silky smooth with eggs, heavenly sweet with sugar, and divinely fiery with sherry."
***Ruth Harvey*, For The Yuletide Feast**

CHAMPAGNE SHERBET PUNCH

3 cups	unsweetened pineapple juice, chilled	750 mL
1/4 cup	ReaLemon lemon juice from concentrate	50 mL
1 qt	pineapple sherbet	1 L
1	bottle Champagne, chilled	750 mL

In a punch bowl, combine pineapple juice and ReaLemon. Just before serving, scoop sherbet in individual scoops into punch bowl and add Champagne. Stir gently. Serve cold. Makes about 2 1/2 qts (2.5 L).

PEPPERMINT STICK PUNCH

1 1/2 cups	sugar	375 mL
1 1/2 cups	ReaLime lime juice from concentrate, chilled	375 mL
1 cup	Vodka or water	250 mL
2 tbsp	white Creme de Menthe	30 mL
	OR	
1/8 tsp	peppermint extract	0.5 mL
	ice block or ice ring	
2-28 oz	bottles club soda	2-750 mL
	peppermint candy canes	

In a punch bowl, dissolve sugar in ReaLime. Stir in Vodka and Creme de Menthe. Just before serving, add ice and stir in club soda. Hang candy canes on edge of bowl and use with each cup as a stirrer. Recipe can be doubled. Serve cold. Makes about 2 1/2 qts (2.5 L).

"England was merry England when
Old Christmas brought his sports again.
'Twas Christmas broach'd the mightiest ale;
'Twas Christmas told the merriest tale;
A Christmas gambol oft could cheer
The poor man's heart through half the year."
  Sir Walter Scott, **Marmion, Canto VI**

FRUIT MEDLEY PUNCH

2-10 oz	packages frozen strawberries in syrup, thawed	2-300 g
3 cups	apricot nectar, chilled	750 mL
3 cups	cold water	750 mL
1 cup	ReaLemon lemon juice from concentrate	250 mL
1-6 1/4 oz	can frozen unsweetened orange juice concentrate, thawed	178 mL
1 cup	sugar	250 mL
1-28 oz	bottle ginger ale, chilled	750 mL
	ice ring (optional)	

In a blender or food processor, purée strawberries well. In a large punch bowl, combine strawberries, apricot nectar, water, ReaLemon, orange juice concentrate and sugar. Stir until sugar dissolves. Slowly pour in ginger ale. Add ice ring. Serve cold. Makes about 3 1/2 qts (3.5 L).

ICE RING

2 1/2 cups	ginger ale, chilled	625 mL
1/2 cup	ReaLemon lemon juice from concentrate	125 mL
	any type of fruit (canned apricot halves, drained; seedless white grapes; strips of orange peel, curled; whole strawberries; mint leaves; Maraschino cherries, drained)	

In a 1 qt (1 L) measure, combine ginger ale and ReaLemon. Pour 1/2 the mixture into a 1 qt (1 L) ring mould. Freeze. Arrange fruits, peel and mint leaves in mould. Pour remaining liquid over fruit and freeze.

"Only what I drink is mine."
Thomas C. Haliburton, **Sam Slick's Wise Saws**

EVERGREEN MINT PUNCH

1 1/2 cups	water	375 mL
1-10 oz	jar mint-flavoured apple jelly	250 mL
3 cups	unsweetened pineapple juice, chilled	750 mL
3/4 cup	ReaLemon lemon juice from concentrate	175 mL
1 1/2 cups	vodka (optional)	375 mL
2-28 oz	bottles ginger ale (lemon-lime)	2-750 mL
1 qt	lime sherbet	1 L

In a small saucepan, combine water and jelly. Cook and stir until jelly melts. Cool. In a large punch bowl, combine jelly mixture with remaining ingredients except sherbet. Stir well. Scoop sherbet into punch bowl in individual scoops. Serve cold. Makes about 4 qts (4 L).

DAD'S QUICK AND EASY EGG NOG

1 qt	commercial egg nog	1 L
1 1/2 cups	dark rum	375 mL
1 cup	heavy cream	250 mL
	nutmeg, grated	

In a punch bowl, combine egg nog with dark rum. In a separate bowl, whip heavy cream and fold into egg nog mixture. Refrigerate until slightly chilled. Sprinkle with nutmeg and serve cold. 12 servings.

EGG NOG

6	eggs, well beaten	
1 qt	milk	1 L
1/2 cup	sugar	125 mL
1/2 tsp	vanilla	2 mL
10 oz	white Rum	300 mL
20 oz	Brandy	600 mL
5 oz	Crème de Café	150 mL

In a bowl, thoroughly blend beaten eggs with milk, sugar, and vanilla. Stir in remaining ingredients. Refrigerate until slightly chilled. Sprinkle with nutmeg and serve cold. Makes about 2 qts (2 L).

Egg nog is the descendant of an English 15th century drink of spiced wine and creamed milk.

RICH EGG NOG

12	eggs, separated	
1 cup	sugar	250 mL
2 cups	rye	500 mL
1 cup	rum	250 mL
4 cups	half-and-half (cream and milk)	1 L
1 cup	whipping cream, whipped and sweetened	250 mL
	nutmeg, grated	

In a mixing bowl, beat egg yolks and 1/2 cup (125 mL) sugar until thick. Whisk in rye, rum, and half-and-half. In a separate bowl beat egg whites until stiff and gradually add 1/2 cup (125 mL) sugar. Gently fold in egg whites and whipped cream and blend thoroughly. Refrigerate until slightly chilled. Sprinkle with nutmeg and serve cold. Makes about 2 qts (2 L).

COFFEE EGG NOG PUNCH

3 cups	cold milk	750 mL
1-14 oz	can Eagle Brand Sweetened Condensed Milk (NOT evaporated milk)	300 mL
4	eggs	
3-4 tsp	instant coffee	15-20 mL
1/3 cup	coffee-flavoured liqueur	75 mL
1 cup	whipping cream, whipped	250 mL
pinch	cinnamon	
pinch	nutmeg, grated	

In a large mixing bowl or food processor, combine milk, Sweetened Condensed Milk, eggs, and coffee. Beat on low speed until coffee dissolves. Stir in bourbon and liqueur and chill. Before serving, top with whipped cream, cinnamon and nutmeg. Coffee and coffee liqueur may be eliminated and bourbon increased to 1/2 cup (125 mL). Makes about 1 1/2 qts (1.5 L).

"Beneath the mistletoe to trade a kiss,
And quaff a cup of eggnog Christmas
day—
If you take out time enough for
this,
Drop in and see us when you pass this
way."
  Lionel Forsyth, invitation to friends at Christmas

On facing page: **Homemade Cream Liqueur** (left), page 19, and **Homemade Irish Cream Liqueur** (right), page 19.

HOMEMADE CREAM LIQUEUR

1-14 oz	can Eagle Brand Sweetened Condensed Milk (NOT evaporated milk)	300 mL
1 1/4 cups	flavoured liqueur (almond, coffee, orange, or mint)	300 mL
1 cup	cream, whipping or coffee	250 mL
4	eggs	
	ice	

In a blender or food processor, combine all ingredients and blend until smooth. Serve over ice and garnish if desired. Store tightly covered in refrigerator up to 1 month. Stir before serving. Makes about 1 qt (1 L).

HOMEMADE IRISH CREAM LIQUEUR

1 3/4 cups	liquor (Irish whiskey, brandy, rum, bourbon, scotch, rye whiskey)	300 mL
1-14 oz	can Eagle Brand Sweetened Condensed Milk (NOT evaporated milk)	300 mL
1 cup	cream, whipping or coffee	250 mL
4	eggs	
2 tbsps	chocolate flavoured syrup	30 mL
2 tsps	instant coffee	10 mL
1 tsp	vanilla extract	5 mL
1/2 tsp	almond extract	2 mL

In a blender or food processor, combine all ingredients and blend until smooth. Serve over ice if desired. Store tightly covered in refrigerator up to 1 month. Stir before serving. Makes about 5 cups (1.25 L).

"Come, bring with a noise,
My merry, merry boys,
The Christmas log to the firing;
While my good dame, she
Bids ye all be free;
And drink to your hearts' desiring."
   Robert Herrick, **Ceremonies For Christmas**

AUNT MARY'S CHEESE AND CINNAMON ROLLS

16	slices bread, crusts removed	
1/4 lb	butter	125g
1-4 oz	package cream cheese	125g
1/4 cup	brown sugar	50 mL
1/4 cup	white sugar	50 mL
2 tsp	cinnamon	10 mL

Roll bread, until thin, with a rolling pin. Butter bread and spread with cream cheese. Roll each slice like a jelly roll. Cover with soft butter and roll in cinnamon mixture. Bake for 6 minutes at 350 F (180 C).

CRAB CANAPES

1-6 oz	can of crab meat	170 g
1/2 cup	mayonnaise	125 mL
1/4 cup	grated cheese	50 mL
2 tbsp	onion, finely chopped	30 mL
1 tbsp	parsley flakes	15 mL
1 tsp	horseradish	5 mL
1 tsp	ketchup	5 mL
1/2 tsp	Worcestershire sauce	2 mL
	melba toast	

In a mixing bowl, combine all ingredients. Spread on melba toast. Place on cookie sheet and heat at 350 F (180 C) for 1 1/2 minutes, or until cheese is melted.

CURRIED CRAB MEAT CANAPES

1/2 tsp	minced onion	2 mL
2 tbsp	butter	25 mL
1 1/2 tsp	flour	7 mL
1/2 tsp	curry powder	2 mL
1/8 tsp	salt	0.5 mL
1/4 cup	light cream	50 mL
1/2 cup	crab meat, flaked	125 mL
4 slices	thin toast	
3 tbsp	Parmesan cheese, grated	45 mL

In a skillet, sauté onion in butter. Mix in flour, curry, and salt. Stir in cream and crab. Remove crusts from toast and quarter. Spread toast with crab mixture and sprinkle with cheese. Place on cookie sheet and broil until cheese melts. Serve hot. Makes 16 pieces.

MUSHROOM BOUCHEES

2 tbsp	minced onion	30 mL
1 cup	mushrooms, sliced	250 mL
4 tbsp	butter	60 mL
4	eggs, hard-cooked	
2 tbsp	dried parsley	30 mL
1 tsp	salt	5 mL
1/8 tsp	pepper	0.5 mL
1	beaten egg	
30	pastry bouchees or toast rounds	
1/2 cup	cheddar cheese, grated	125 mL

In a skillet, sauté onion and mushrooms in butter. Add remaining ingredients and cook until thick. Spoon into bouchées and top with grated cheese. Warm in oven and then broil until cheese melts. Serve hot. Makes 30 pieces.

MUSHROOM PASTRIES

1/2 lb	mushrooms, sliced	250 g
1/4 cup	butter	50 mL
2	beef boullion cubes	
1/2 cup	boiling water	125 mL
3 tbsp	flour	50 mL
1/4-1/2 cup	water	50-125 mL
1/4 tsp	salt	1 mL
2 tsp	caraway seeds (optional)	10 mL
1	egg, beaten	
1 tbsp	cold water	15 mL
	unbaked pastry	

In a skillet, saute mushrooms in butter. Add boullion cubes dissolved in boiling water. In a small bowl, make a smooth paste of flour and water and stir into boullion mixture until thick. Add salt and caraway seeds. Combine thoroughly and chill. Line a 13 x 9 x 2'' (3 L) pan with unbaked pastry. Spread mushroom filling on top and cover with a thin sheet of pastry. Seal edges with fingers and prick pastry with fork. Brush with beaten egg diluted with 1 tbsp (15 mL) water. Bake for 20 minutes, until lightly browned, at 425 F (220 C). Cut in squares or triangles and serve hot.

"Réveillon" is the French-Canadian Christmas Eve celebration.

SPINACH CHEESE SQUARES

4 tbsp.	butter, melted	60 mL
3	eggs	
1 cup	flour	250 mL
1 cup	milk	250 mL
1 tsp	baking powder	5 mL
1 tsp	salt	5 mL
3/4 lb	Edam cheese, grated	750 g
2-10 oz	packages frozen spinach, drained and chopped	2-283 g

In a 13 x 9 x 2'' (3.5 L) pan, place melted butter and coat the bottom the pan. In a mixing bowl, beat eggs. Add flour, milk, baking powder and salt. Mix thoroughly. Add cheese and spinach. Spread mixture in pan. Bake at 350 F (180 C) for 45 minutes. Cut in squares and serve hot. Freezes well. Can be made ahead and warmed up.

GREEK SQUARES

2 lbs	spinach	1 kg
1	medium onion, chopped	
3 tbsp	butter	45 mL
5	eggs, beaten	
1 1/2 cups	feta cheese, crumbled	375 mL
1/3 cup	parsley, chopped fine	75 mL
1/2 tsp	salt	2 mL
	pepper to taste	
pinch	nutmeg	
20	sheets of phyllo pastry	20
2/3 cup	butter, melted	150 mL

Thoroughly wash spinach and chop into small pieces, discarding stems. In a large skillet, saute onion in butter. Add spinach pieces and continue to saute until spinach is wilted. Cool and drain. Stir in eggs, cheese, parsley, salt and spices and mix thoroughly. Lightly grease a 9 x 13 x 2'' (3.5 L) pan. Place 10 layers of phyllo pastry in the pan, brushing each sheet with melted butter. Allow pastry to overhang the pan. Spread spinach mixture on top. Cut remaining phyllo sheets so they will fit the pan exactly. Place 10 layers of phyllo pastry on top of the spinach layer, brushing each sheet with melted butter. Form overhang into an edge. Cover with foil and bake for 50 minutes at 350 F (180 C). Remove the foil and continue baking for 10 minutes. Cut in squares and serve hot.

STUFFED OLIVES

Wrap bacon around olives and secure with toothpicks. Broil and serve when bacon is done.

SALMON PARTY BALL

1-7.5 oz	can salmon	213 g
1-8 oz	package cream cheese	250 g
1 tbsp	ReaLemon juice from concentrate	15 mL
1 tbsp	grated onion	15 mL
2 tsp	horseradish	10 mL
1/4 tsp	salt	10 mL
1/4 tsp	hot pepper sauce	1 mL
1/4 tbsp	Worcestershire sauce	5 mL
1/2 cup	pecans, chopped (optional)	125 mL
3 tbsp	dried parsley	45 mL

In a mixing bowl, cream together salmon, cream cheese, and lemon juice. Add remaining ingredients except for parsley. Form ingredients into a ball and roll in parsley. Refrigerate. Serve at room temperature with an assortment of crackers.

TUNA BALL

6	eggs, hard-boiled, finely chopped	
2-8 oz	packages cream cheese	2-250 g
2-7 oz	cans tuna, drained	2-198
1/4 cup	green onion, minced	50 mL
2 tbsp	dried parsley	30 mL
2 tbsp	Worcestershire sauce	30 mL
2 tbsp	ReaLemon juice from concentrate	30 mL
1/2 tsp	salt	2 mL
6 tbsp	dried parsley	90 mL

In a mixing bowl, cream together eggs and tuna. Add remaining ingredients. Chill 2 hours. Shape into 2 balls and roll in parsley. Serve at room temperature with a variety of crackers.

PARTY CHEESE BALL

2-8 oz	packages cream cheese	2-250 g
2 tbsp	season salt	30 mL
1-18 oz	can crushed pineapple, drained	540 mL
2-4 oz	packages pecans, chopped	2-100 g
1	green pepper, finely chopped	
1	onion, diced	

In a mixing bowl, combine all ingredients except pecans. Form into a ball. Roll ball in pecans and refrigerate. Serve at room temperature with an assortment of crackers.

CHEDDAR CHEESE BALL

1 lb	sharp cheddar cheese, shredded	500 g
2 oz	blue cheese, crumbled	60 g
2 tbsp	Worcestershire sauce	30 mL
1 tbsp	onion, finely chopped	15 mL
1/2 cup	mayonnaise	125 mL
5 drops	hot pepper sauce	
1 cup	walnuts finely chopped	250 ml
1/4 cup	dried parsley	50 mL
1/2 tsp	paprika	2 mL

In a mixing bowl, thoroughly blend cheeses. Add Worcestershire sauce, onion, mayonnaise and hot pepper sauce. Chill 2 hours and shape into a ball. In a small bowl, combine walnuts, parsley and paprika. Roll cheese ball in walnut mixture and refrigerate. Serve at room temperature with an assortment of crackers.

SHERRY CHEESE LOG

3 tbsp	Sherry (brandy)	45 mL
1/2 cup	soft butter	125 mL
2/3 cup	blue cheese, crumbled	150 mL
1-4 oz	package cream cheese	125 g
2 tbsp	Parmesan cheese, grated	30 mL
3 drops	Tobasco	
1-4 oz	package pecans, finely chopped	100 g

In a blender or food processor, combine sherry and butter. Gradually add remaining ingredients, except pecans, and blend until smooth. Form mixture into the shape of a log. Roll log in pecans and refrigerate.Serve at room temperature with an assortment of crackers.

NIPPY CHEDDAR SPREAD

1 lb	sharp Cheddar cheese, grated	500 g
1-8 oz	package cream cheese, softened	250 g
1/2 cup	horseradish	125 mL
1 tsp	Tobasco	5 mL
1 tbsp	cream	15 mL
1/2 cup	medium dry Sherry	125 mL

Blend cheeses by hand or in a food processor. Add remaining ingredients and blend until smooth. Place in a serving dish or sealed container and chill. Serve at room temperature with an assortment of crackers.

"Ceilidh" is the Scottish New Year celebration.

SPECIAL CHEESE SPREAD

2 lb	sharp Cheddar cheese, shredded	1 kg
2 tbsp	dried parsley	30 mL
2 tbsp	dried chives	30 mL
2 tbsp	thyme	30 mL
1/2 cup	whipping cream	125 mL
1 cup	Sherry	250 mL
2 tbsp	sage	30 mL
2 tbsp	savory	30 mL

In a mixing bowl, blend all ingredients until smooth. Refrigerate for 3 days. Remix in a blender or food processor and pack into serving dishes. Refrigerate until serving. Serve at room temperature with an assortment of crackers.

RUM SPREAD

1 lb	Cheddar cheese, grated	500 g
1/2 cup	butter	125 mL
2 tbsp	rum	30 mL
1/8 tsp	cayenne pepper	0.5 mL

In a mixing bowl, thoroughly blend all ingredients. Pack firmly into serving dishes and refrigerate. Serve at room temperature with an assortment of crackers. For variety, add chopped walnuts, olives, onions, dill, or caraway seeds.

WALNUT AND HERB SPREAD

1-8 oz	package cream cheese	250 g
1/4 lb	Cheddar cheese, shredded	125 g
3/8 cup	walnuts, finely chopped	75 mL
1 tsp	onion, grated	5 mL
1/2 tsp	garlic powder	2 mL
1/8 tsp	rosemary	0.5 mL
1/8 tsp	thyme	0.5 mL
pinch	salt, pepper	

In a mixing bowl, thoroughly blend all ingredients. Pack firmly into serving dishes and refrigerate. Serve at room temperature with a variety of crackers.

Mistletoe was first gathered with great ceremony by the Druids and hung in their homes.

HAM SPREAD

1-4 1/2 oz	can devilled ham	115 g
1/4 tsp	curry powder	1 mL
1-8 oz	package cream cheese	250 g
1/2 cup	chopped chutney	125 mL

In a mixing bowl, thoroughly blend all ingredients. Refrigerate and serve at room temperature with an assortment of crackers or rippled potatoe chips.

OYSTER CHEESE SPREAD

1-4 oz	package cream cheese	125 g
1-4 oz	jar smoked oysters, chopped	113 g
1 tbsp	mayonnaise	15 mL
1 tbsp	sherry	15 mL
1 tsp	onion juice	5 mL
1/2 tsp	paprika	2 mL
	chives, finely minced	

In a mixing bowl, thoroughly combine all ingredients except chives. Pack into a serving dish and garnish with chives. Refrigerate. Serve at room temperature with toast rounds.

MUSHROOM SPREAD

2-4 oz	packages cream cheese	2-125 g
1 tbsp	onion, minced	15 mL
1 cup	mushrooms, finely chopped	250 mL
1/2 tsp	curry powder	2 mL
	dried parsley	

In a mixing bowl, cream together cream cheese and onion. Add mushrooms and curry powder. Pack into a serving dish and garnish with parsley. Refrigerate. Serve at room temperature with a variety of crackers or spread on open faced sandwiches.

"I wish we could put some of the Christmas spirit in jars and open a jar of it every month."
Harlan Miller

HOT CRAB PUFFS

1 cup	mayonnaise	250 mL
1 cup	crab meat, flaked	250 mL
2	egg whites, beaten to peaks	
30	pastry bouchées or toast rounds	
pinch	paprika	

In a bowl, combine mayonnaise and crab meat. Fold into egg whites. Spoon into bouchees and sprinkle with paprika. Broil 3 minutes until puffy and lightly browned. Serve hot. Makes 30 pieces.

ELIZABETH'S CRAB SPREAD

1-6 oz	can crab meat, drained	170 g
3	hard boiled eggs	
1	green onion, finely chopped	
pinch	salt, pepper	
	mayonnaise to taste	

Grate hard boiled eggs through a cheese grater. In a mixing bowl, combine crab meat and eggs. Add green onion, salt and pepper and combine well. Add enough mayonnaise for creamy consistency. Refrigerate overnight. Serve with an assortment of crackers.

LIVERWURST PARTY SPREAD

8 oz	liverwurst	250 g
1-8 oz	package cream cheese	250 g
1/4 cup	onions, chopped	50 mL
2 tbsp	pickles, chopped (sweet or dill)	30 mL
2 tbsp	milk	30 mL
1-4 oz	package cream cheese	125 g
1/4 cup	walnuts, finely chopped	50 mL
	dried parsley	

In a mixing bowl, cream together liverwurst, 8 oz (250 mg) cream cheese, onions, and pickles. Shape into a ball. In a small bowl, combine milk and cream cheese. Coat ball with cream cheese mixture. Sprinkle with nuts and parsley and refrigerate. Serve at room temperature with an assortment of crackers.

Louis Prang created the first American Christmas card in 1873. One special card he designed for his family and friends was painted by Mrs. O.E. Whitney and autographed by Charles Dickens.

LIVER PATE

1 lb	chicken livers	500 g
1 lb	mushrooms, sliced	500 g
1/2 cup	onions, chopped	125 mL
4 tbsp	butter	60 mL
1/4 cup	brandy	50 mL
1/4 tsp	nutmeg, grated	1 ml
1 tsp	garlic salt	5 mL
1/8 tsp	cloves	0.5 mL
1/4 tsp	cayenne pepper	1 mL
pinch	salt	

In a skillet, sauté chicken livers, mushrooms and onions in butter. Place remaining ingredients in blender or food processor and blend thoroughly. Add liver mixture and continue to blend. Pack firmly into serving dishes and refrigerate. Serve at room temperature with a variety of crackers.

SMOKED SALMON PATE

1/2 cup	butter, melted	125 mL
1/4 lb	smoked slamon	250 g
3	egg yolks	
1 tbsp	ReaLemon juice from concentrate	15 mL
	pepper to taste	

In a saucepan, heat butter until very hot. Chop salmon into small pieces. In a blender or food processor, beat egg yolks. Add butter very gradually and blend slowly. Add salmon, lemon juice and pepper and purée. Pack firmly into a serving dish and chill at least 4 hours before serving. Serve on toast rounds or melba toast.

The first Christmas card created for general distribution was etched in England on December 9th, 1842, by 16 year old William Maw Egley Jr. The card is preserved in the British Museum and reads ''Merry Christmas And A Happy New Year To You''.

KATHLEEN'S FAMILY-SECRET CLAM DIP

1-8 oz	package cream cheese, softened	250 g
2 tbsp	mayonnaise	30 mL
2 tbsp	Sherry or Port	30 mL
2 cups	minced clams, drained	500 mL
1/2 tsp	curry powder	2 mL
pinch	salt	
pinch	garlic powder	
pinch	onion salt	
1/2 tsp	chives, chopped	2 mL

In a mixing bowl, blend cream cheese and mayonnaise. Add Sherry and mix thoroughly. Add clams and spices, except for chives. Place mixture in an oven-proof dish and bake at 325 F (160 C) for 15 minutes to a half hour. Remove from oven and sprinkle with chives. Serve hot with an assortment of crackers.

MOULDED SHRIMP DIP

1/2 cup	boiling water	125 mL
1-3 oz	package lemon jello	85 g
2-4-3/4 oz	cans shrimp, drained and chopped	2-115 g
1 cup	celery, chopped	250 mL
1/2 cup	light cream	125 mL
1	onion, finely chopped	
2	pimentos, finely chopped	
2	eggs, hard-cooked, finely chopped	
1 cup	mayonnaise	250 mL
1-4 oz	package pimento cream cheese	125 g

In a mixing bowl, dissolve jello in boiling water. Place jello in a blender or food processor and add remaining ingredients. Blend until smooth. Pour into a buttered 4 cup (1 L) mould and chill until firm. Serve with an assortment of crackers.

Up until 1900, Christmas cards were generally not signed or mailed, but hand delivered with a calling card.

CURRIED CRAB MEAT DIP

1-4.23 oz	can crab meat, flaked	120 g
1/2 cup	mayonnaise	125 mL
1/4 tsp	curry powder	1 mL
3 drops	Tobasco	
3 shakes	cayenne pepper	

In a mixing bowl, combine all ingredients and blend thoroughly. Refrigerate. Serve with an assortment of crackers.

HOT AND SPICY FONDUE DIP

1-4 oz.	can green chilies, chopped	114 mL
3	cooking onions, chopped	
2 tbsp.	butter	30 mL
2-10 oz.	cans Cheddar cheese soup	2-284 mL
1/4 cup	milk	50 mL
1	medium tomato, chopped	
pinch	salt, pepper, garlic powder	

In a skillet, sauté chilies and onions in butter. In a saucepan, combine soup and milk until blended. Add chilies and onions to soup mixture and cook 10 minutes. Add tomato and spices and continue to heat until tomato is hot. Serve in a fondue pot to keep dip hot. Serve with tacos and an assortment of raw vegetables.

The Romans were the first people to decorate their homes and temples with green boughs and flowers in the week long celebration of Saturnalia.

SPINACH DIP

1	package of Knorr's vegetable soup mix	74 g
1 cup	mayonnaise	250 mL
1 1/2 cups	sour cream	375 mL
1-14 oz	can of water chestnuts, chopped	398 mL
1-10 oz	package frozen spinach, drained, chopped, uncooked	300 g
1	round of Italian bread	

In a mixing bowl, combine all ingredients except bread, several hours before serving. Hollow out round of Italian bread and cut into 1″ (2.5 cm) cubes. Fill round with chilled dip and serve with bread cubes.

RAW VEGETABLE DIP

1-4 oz	package cream cheese	125 g
1	envelope dry onion soup mix	
1 cup	sour cream	250 mL
1/4 cup	filberts, finely chopped	50 mL

In a mixing bowl, combine all ingredients thoroughly. Refrigerate and serve with raw vegetables.

Up until 1914, it was an English custom to send booklets containing poems to friends at Christmas.

AVOCADO SOUP

2	ripe avocados	
1 cup	chicken broth	250 mL
1 1/2 cups	heavy cream	375 mL
1/2 cup	dry, white wine	125 mL
1 tsp	ReaLemon lemon juice from concentrate	5 mL
	salt, white pepper to taste	
1/2 tsp	dill	2 mL

Halve, pit, and peel avocados and mash the pulp. In a saucepan, heat chicken broth. Remove broth from heat and blend in avocado. Purée mixture in a blender or a food processor. Place purée in a large bowl and add cream, wine, lemon juice, salt and pepper. Cover and chill until serving. Garnish individual servings with dill. Serve cold. 4 servings.

POTATO LEAK SOUP

1	large potato, sliced thin like scalloped potatoes	
2	leaks, whites only, sliced in rings	
	water	
1 tbsp	cornstarch	15 mL
1-10 oz	can chicken broth	284 mL
1 cup	milk	250 mL
2 tbsp	butter	30 mL
	salt, pepper, to taste	

In a large saucepan, place potato and leaks with just enough water to cover them and boil until the potato is cooked. In a measuring cup, combine cornstarch with just enough water to make a smooth paste. To potato mixtue, add chicken broth, milk and butter and thicken with cornstarch paste. Add salt and pepper. Serve hot. 4 servings.

"Sviata Vecheria" is the Ukranian Holy Supper celebration.

CREAM OF CARROT SOUP

2 tbsp	butter	30 mL
1	medium onion, finely chopped	
6	medium carrots, diced	
5 tbsp	flour	75 mL
6 cups	chicken stock	1.5 L
1 tsp	salt	5 mL
1	bay leaf	
1/4 tsp	crushed thyme	1 mL
2	stalks parsley	
1/2 tsp	sugar	2 mL
1 cup	milk	250 mL
1/2 cup	heavy cream	125 mL
3 tbsp	finely chopped parsley and chives, mixed	45 mL

In a large saucepan, melt butter. Add onions and brown over a low heat. Cover 1 minute. Add carrots and continue to cook over a low heat for 15 minutes. Stir in flour and cook 2-3 minutes, stirring to prevent scorching. In a small saucepan, heat chicken stock stirring constantly. Add salt, spices, except for parsley and chives, and sugar. Simmer uncovered for 15 minutes. Remove bay leaf and parsley. In a small saucepan, scald milk and cream. Add to chicken stock and blend thoroughly. Add this mixture gradually to carrots and onions. Stir over low heat until soup is smooth. Garnish with chopped parsley and chives. Serve hot. 8 servings.

VICHYSSOISE

6	leeks, whites only, thinly sliced	
2	small onions, thinly sliced	
1	stalk celery, diced	
1/2 cup	water	125 mL
4 cups	chicken broth	1 L
5	potatoes, diced	
2 cups	milk, scalded	500 mL
1 tsp	salt	5 mL
1 tsp	white pepper	5 mL
1 cup	cream	250 mL
	chives, chopped	
	Worcestershire sauce	

In a large saucepan, cook leeks, onions, and celery in water for 5 minutes. Add chicken broth and potatoes and cook 15 minutes more. Add scalded milk and bring soup almost to a boil. Season and then purée soup in an electric blender or food processor. Refrigerate. Add cream only when serving. Garnish with chives and a drop of Worcestershire sauce. Serve cold. 8 servings.

Christmas day, 1642, Sir Isaac Newton was born.

CHRISTMAS EVE OYSTER SOUP

3 qt	milk	3 L
4 tbsp	flour	60 mL
3 tsp	salt	15 mL
1/4 tsp	pepper	1 mL
1/4 cup	water	50 mL
1 qt	shucked stewing oysters, in their own liquor	1 L
3 tbsp	butter	45 mL

In a large saucepan, heat milk until scalded and set aside. In a small jar, combine flour, salt, pepper and water and shake until smooth. Place oysters in their liquor in a saucepan and slowly add flour mixture stirring constantly. Heat only a few minutes until mixture thickens and oysters begin to curl around the edges. Pour oyster mixture into hot milk. Add butter and serve immediately. Makes 4 qts (4 L). 16-1 cup (250 mL) servings.

CHRISTMAS SOUP

2-10 oz	cans consommé	2-284 mL
3 cups	tomato juice	750 mL
1 tbsp	ReaLemon lemon juice from concentrate	15 mL
6	cloves	
1	bay leaf	
1/2 tsp	salt	2 mL
1 tsp	sugar	5 mL
1/4 tsp	Accent (optional)	1 mL
2 tbsp	sweet Sherry	30 mL

In a large saucepan, combine consommé, tomato juice, ReaLemon, cloves and bay leaf. Simmer for 10 minutes and strain. Add salt, sugar and Accent and bring to a boil. Add Sherry and serve in punch glasses. 8 servings.

The Saxons were the first people to decorate with holly, ivy and bay at Christmas.

On facing page: **Christmas Soup** (top), page 34, and **Seafood Salad** (bottom), page 37.

CRAB AND AVOCADO APPETIZER

1/2 lb	crab meat, flaked	250 g
1/2 cup	mayonnaise	125 mL
2 tsp	ReaLemon juice from concentrate	10 mL
1 tbsp	light cream	15 mL
2	large avocados	
	mayonnaise to taste	

In a mixing bowl, blend crab meat and mayonnaise. Add lemon juice and cream and mix thoroughly. Dice avocados and toss lightly with crab mixture. Refrigerate and serve in cocktail glasses, topped with mayonnaise. 6 servings.

HOT SEAFOOD SALAD

1 cup	fine dry bread crumbs	250 mL
2 tbsp	butter, melted	30 mL
1 cup	crab meat, flaked	250 mL
1/2 cup	onions, finely chopped	125 mL
1 cup	celery, chopped	250 mL
1/4 cup	minced onion	50 mL
1/2	green pepper, chopped (optional)	
1/2 cup	mayonnaise	125 mL
1 tsp	Worcestershire sauce	5 mL
1/2 tsp	salt	2 mL
1/2 tsp	pepper	2 mL

In a small bowl, combine bread crumbs and melted butter and set aside. In a mixing bowl, thoroughly combine all ingredients and place in a 1 1/2 qt (1.5 L) buttered casserole dish. Top with bread crumb mixture and bake for 20-30 minutes at 350 F (180 C). Or place ingredients in individual seafood shells or ramekins and top with buttered crumbs. Bake for 10-15 minutes at 350 F (180 C). 6 servings.

The tradition of kissing under the mistletoe is thought by some to lead inevitably to marriage.

Christmas Dinner

ABOUT POULTRY

Market dressed = insides, head, and feet of bird have not been removed.

Ready-to-cook = head and feet have been removed, insides have been removed (drawn), giblets have been cleaned.

22 lb (11 kg) market dressed = 18 lb (9 kg) ready-to-cook

Refrigerator Thawing
Leave original wrapper on bird and place on a tray. Allow 24 hours thawing time for each 5 lbs (2.5 kg) of bird.

Cold-water Thawing
Leave original wrapper on bird and fully emerge in sink in cold water. Change water every 30 minutes. Allow 30 minutes of thawing time for every pound (0.5 kg) of bird.

ready-to-cook weight in lb	in kg	in refrigerator	under cold water
4–12	2–6	1–2 days	4–6 hours
12–20	6–10	2–3 days	6–8 hours
20–24	10–12	3–4 days	8–12 hours

Refrigerate thawed bird until ready to use.

Use bird within 24 hours of thawing.

Joseph Tomalin, born Christmas Eve, 1846, in England, emigrated to Toronto in 1871 and was the first merchant to set up a stall at the St. Lawrence market. A poultry dealer, he specialized in turkeys. He advertised hisCanadian "wild turkeys" in London, England, and made 6 profitable Christmas trips to England, via the train to Halifax and ship to England. His turkeys sold out at once.

ROAST TURKEY

Turkey weighing 12 lb (6 kg) or less (drawn & dressed), allow 1 lb (500 g) per serving.

Turkey weighing more than 12 lb (6 kg) (drawn & dressed), allow 3/4 lb (375 g) per serving.

Boneless turkey breast, allow 4 oz (125 g) per serving.

TURKEY FACTS

20 lb (10 kg) drawn = 7 1/2 lb (3.75 kg) meat. Hens weigh 6-16 lb (3-8 kg). Toms weigh 12 lb (6 kg) and more.

FOR BEST RESULTS

RINSE bird in cold water and towel dry.

MOISTEN skin and cavity with lemon juice.

STUFF cavity through body opening. Secure with skewers or sew with thread.

BUTTER turkey generously.

PLACE bird in roasting pan, on a rack, keeping bird out of its own juices, allowing more even cooking.

For *MEAT THERMOMETER* cooking, insert thermometer in center of inside of thigh; bulb must not touch bone.

BASTE turkey every 30 minutes; pre-basted turkeys require no basting.

Turkey is *DONE* when juice runs clear in colour when the meat is pricked with a fork; drumstick twists easily in the socket; meat feels soft to the touch.

Before *CARVING*, let turkey stand 20-30 minutes. Juices will retreat into the meat, resulting in a more moist turkey, and carving is easier.

The turkey came to be eaten at Christmas when it was brought by Spanish ships to Spain, in 1519, from the Aztecs in Mexico.

How bless'd, how envied, were our life.
Could we but scape the poulterer's knife!
But man, curs'd man, on Turkeys preys,
And Christmas shortens all our days:
Sometimes with oysters we combine,
Sometimes assist the savoury chine;
From the low peasant to the lord,
The Turkey smokes on every board.
     John Gay, Fables: **The Turkey And The Ant**

COOKING METHOD I (covered)

COVER bird loosely with foil or greased brown paper.
COOK for 20-30 minutes at 450 F (230 C).
REDUCE heat to 325 F (160 C) and continue cooking:

birds up to 11 lb (5.5 kg)	20 minutes per lb (40–45 minutes per kg)
birds 11–15 lb (5.5–7.5 kg)	18 minutes per lb (36 minutes per kg)
birds over 15 lb (7.5 kg)	16 minutes per lb (34 minutes per kg)

COOKING METHOD II (uncovered)

ROAST bird uncovered and baste frequently.

ready-to-cook weight in lb	in kg	roasting time uncovered in hours
6–8	3–4	4–4 1/2
8–10	4–5	4 1/2–5 1/2
10–13	5–6.5	5 1/2–6 1/2
13–16	6.5–8	6 1/4–6 3/4
16–20	8–10	6 3/4–7 1/4
20–24	10–12	7 1/4–8

COOKING METHOD III (with roasting pan cover)

ROAST bird covered with lid. Remove lid last hour of cooking.

ready-to-cook weight in lb	in kg	roasting time covered in hours
6–8	3–4	3–3 1/2
8–10	4–5	3 1/2–4
10–13	5–6.5	4 1/4–5
13–16	6.5–8	5–5 3/4
16–20	8–10	6–6 1/4
20–24	10–12	7–7 1/4

COOKING METHOD IV (with meat thermometer)

ROAST bird in 325 F (160 C) oven until thermometer registers 180-185 F.

Legend has it that Clement C. Moore began composing "The Night Before Christmas" while on a trip to market, by sleigh, to buy the Christmas turkey. This poem is the origin of Santa arriving by sleigh.

ROAST CHICKEN

Allow 1/2–1/4 lb (125-250 g) (drawn & dressed) per serving per meal.

CHICKEN FACTS

roasting chickens weigh 3-6 lb (1.5-3 kg)
capon chickens weigh 6 lb (3 kg) and more

FOR BEST RESULTS

RINSE bird in cold water and towel dry.
COAT with salt and pepper and spread with butter.

COOKING METHOD I (covered)

STUFF cavity through neck opening and secure with skewers or sew with thread.

BUTTER chicken generously.

PLACE bird in roasting pan with 3-4 tbsp (45-60 mL) water.

COVER bird loosely with foil or greased brown paper.

COOK 20 minutes per lb (40 minutes per kg) at 350 F (180 C).

BASTE every 20 minutes.

Christmas dinner was traditionally the only meal of the day, and consisted of two main courses, a bird and a pudding.

COOKING METHOD II (without dressing)

FRESH choice chicken is best without dressing.

SPRINKLE cavity with oregano and place several peeled garlic cloves inside.

MELT 1/4 cup (50 mL) butter in roasting pan and roll chicken in butter; sprinkle bird with salt and pepper and place breast side down in pan.

ROAST approximately 15 minutes per lb (30 minutes per kg) at 400 F (200 C).

REDUCE oven temperature to 300 F (150 C) and roast 1 hour more.

SQUEEZE ReaLemon lemon juice from concentrate over entire bird; cover and cook 15 minutes longer.

SPRINKLE bird with 1/2 tsp (2 mL) oregano before serving.

COOKING METHOD III (uncovered)

ready-to-cook weight in lb	in kg	cooking time in hours
2 1/2–3 1/2	1.25–1.75	2
3 1/2–5	1.75–2.5	3
5 1/2	2.75	3 3/4

PREHEAT oven to 450 F (230 C).

REDUCE heat to 350 F (180 C).

COOK UNCOVERED.

"Now capons and hens, besides turkeys and ducks, with beef and mutton—must all die, for in twelve days a multitude of people will not be fed with little."
Washington Irving, The Christmas Coach

"And now two smaller Cratchits, boy and girl, came tearing in, screaming that outside the baker's they had smelt the goose, and known it for their own; and basking in luxurious thoughts of sage and onion, these young Cratchits danced about the table . . .
Charles Dickens, A Christmas Carol

"Christmas is coming, the geese are getting fat,
Please to put a penny in the old man's hat;
If you haven't got a penny, a ha'penny will do,
If you haven't got a ha'penny, God bless you!"
  Beggar's Rhyme

ROAST GOOSE

Allow 1-1 1/4 lb (500-625 g) (drawn & dressed) per serving per meal.

FOR BEST RESULTS

RINSE bird in cold water and scrub skin with 1 qt (1 L) water and 1 tsp (5 mL) baking soda; rinse and towel dry.

REMOVE any large fat layers from skin.

SPRINKLE cavity with salt and pepper.

STUFF neck cavity first and secure neck skin with skewer.

FILL body cavity and secure with skewer or sew with thread.

NON-DRESSED bird, place several apples, cut in half, in cavity.

TIE ends of legs taut against body.

PRICK skin only, with fork near legs and wings to release fat, not juice, during cooking.

LIGHTLY season skin with salt and pepper.

GOOSE is done when legs pull easily; drumstick meat feels soft; juice from drumsticks runs pale yellow.

SERVE half an hour after bird has finished cooking.

BEFORE taking goose to table, turn breast side down and find hip joints, located almost at backbone. Loosen legs at these joints; cut meat free from bone above these joints. Arrange goose, breast side up, and take to table for carving.

"For the goose is man's comfort in peace, sleepinge and wakinge."
Roger Ascham, Tutor to Queen Elizabeth I
COOKING METHOD I (covered)

COVER bottom of pan with water and cider vinegar.

PLACE bird right side up in pan and cover loosely with foil or greaseproof paper.

BASTE every 20 minutes.

DRAIN fat at least twice, as it accumulates.

"There is no more tantalizing aroma in all cookery than the smell of a fine goose, browning slowly in the oven."
Silas Spitzer, The Festive Christmas Goose
COOKING METHOD II (uncovered)

PLACE bird uncovered, breast side down, on roasting rack in roasting pan.

SPOON off fat as it accumulates in pan; turn breast side up after 2/3 of cooking.

In France the Christmas goose is rubbed inside and out with good red Wine and garlic

COOKING METHODS I & II AT 325 F (160 C)

ready-to-cook weight in lb	in kg	roasting time in hours
4–6	2–2.5	2–3
7–8	3–3.5	3 1/2–4
9–11	4–5	4–4 1/2
12–14	5.5–6.5	5–5 3/4

"A glorious goose fattened on the rice bed in our lake, was killed for the occasion: turkeys were only to be met with on old cleared farms, in those days, and beef was rarely seen in the backwoods."
Catherine Parr Traill, The Canadian Settler's Guide

ROAST DUCK

Allow 1-1 1/4 lb (500-625 g) (drawn & dressed) per serving per meal.

FOR BEST RESULTS

RINSE bird in cold water and towel dry.

REMOVE any large fat layers from skin.

SPRINKLE cavity with salt and pepper.

STUFF cavity through neck opening; secure with skewers or sew with thread.

LIGHTLY season bird with salt and pepper; spread small amount of butter on breast.

PRICK skin only, with fork near legs and wings to release fat, not juice, during cooking.

COOKING METHOD I (uncovered)

PLACE bird breast side down on greased rack in roasting pan.

ROAST 10 minutes at 450 F (230 C), until back is golden. Turn and continue cooking 10 minutes until golden.

DRAIN excess fat.

LOWER oven temperature to 350 F (180 C) and continue to cook at least 1 1/2 hours.

COOKING METHOD II (covered)

COVER bottom of pan with water and cider vinegar.

PLACE bird right side up in roasting pan and cover loosely with foil or greaseproof paper.

BASTE every 20 minutes.

DRAIN fat at least twice, as it accumulates.

Sir Henry Grey's pie, made in London in 1770, was nine feet in circumference. It weighed 12 stone and was pushed into the dining hall on wheels. It consisted of: 4 geese, 4 wild ducks, 2 woodcocks, 2 turkeys, 4 partridges, 7 blackbirds, 6 pigeons, 2 rabbits, 2 neat's tongues, 2 bushels of flour, and 20 pounds of butter.

ready-to-cook weight in lb	in kg	roasting time in hours
2–3	1–1.5	1 1/2–2
3–5	1.5–2.5	2–2 1/2

BROIL bird 10 minutes if crisp brown skin is desired.

ADD Port Wine to gravy.

ROAST PHEASANT

2 birds serve 4-6 people

FOR BEST RESULTS

RINSE bird in cold water and towel dry.

BUTTER bird inside and out.

TIE bacon fat over breast.

ROAST quickly, both birds in the same pan, for 45 minutes to 1 hour at 375 F (190 C).

BASTE frequently.

REMOVE bacon fat last 10 minutes.

King Arthur's table, set by Whistlecraft
"...salmon, venison, and wild boars,
by hundreds, and by dozens and by scores.
Hogsheads of honey, Kilderkins of mustard,
Muttons, and fatted beeves, and bacon swine;
Herons and bitterns, peacocks, swan, and bustard,
Teal, mallard, pigeons, widgeons, and in fine,
Plum-puddings, pancakes, apple-pies, and custard.
And therewi'thal they drank good Gascon Wine,
With mead, and ale, and cider of our own;
For porter, punch, and negus were not known."

ROAST BEEF

allow 1/2 lb (250 g) (with bone) per serving per meal, and 1/4 lb (125 g) (without bone) per serving per meal

BEEF FACTS

PREFER roast with bone.

COOK slowly without searing to reduce shrinkage.

FOR BEST RESULTS

SPRINKLE roast with salt.

PLACE fat side up in roasting pan.

BASTE occasionally.

COOKING TIMES

type of roast	minutes per lb (500 g)	
standing rib	rare	23
(with bone)	medium	27
	well done	34
rolled rib, loin	rare	32
(without bone)	medium	35
	well done	40

"If roast beef held the place of honor, it was seven ribs thick, and loomed in its platter like Gibraltar."
Silas Spitzer, The Feast Of Christmas

CROWN ROAST OF LAMB

allow 2 ribs per serving

FOR BEST RESULTS

DRESS center or crown with stuffing.

PLACE weighted bowl on dressing to retain shape.

SEASON roast with salt and pepper.

COOK 30-40 minutes per lb (1-1 1/2 hr per kg) at 325 F (160 C).

BEFORE serving, garnish ends of ribs with paper frills or crab apples.

BAKED HAM

allow 1/2 lb (250 g) (with bone) per serving per meal, and 1/4 lb (125 g) (without bone) per serving per meal

FOR BEST RESULTS

DETERMINE type of ham and cook according to directions on package or according to appropriate *METHODS I, II, OR III*.

SCORE fat in diamond shapes, not too deep, as they deepen upon cooking.

PLACE whole cloves in each corner of diamond for added flavour and decoration.

GLAZE ham only after cooking. Glaze pre-cooked ham only after thorough warming in oven.

"The house grew redolent with the varied aromas of pastry and spices; the cupboards began to fill up with danties; along the shelves of the cold-pantry were ranged dozens of fat meat-pies, enormous cooked hams and assorted roasts, platters of meat-balls, pea soup enriched with hulled corn and the delicate leaves of sarriette . . ."

Corinne Rocheleau Rouleau, **When Heaven Smiled On Our World**

COOKING METHOD I (picnic hams, cottage rolls)

SIMMER ham in a generous amount of water.

ALLOW 30 minutes per lb (60 minutes per kg).

TO SERVE COLD let stand for 1 hour in water. Remove from water and continue to cool.

GLAZE when cool.

COOKING METHOD II (oven cooking)

PLACE ham fat side down on rack in covered roasting pan.

ADD 2 cups of water around ham.

COOKING TIMES

type of ham	weight in lb	in kg	minutes per lb	per kg
with bone				
whole	8–10	3.5–4.5	18–20	36–40
	10–15	4.5–6.5	18	36
	15–18	6.5–9	15	35
half	5–8	2.5–4	25	50
without bone				
whole	8–10	3.5–4.5	25	50
half	4–5	2–2.5	30	60

COOKING METHOD III (mild cured hams)

WRAP ham in aluminum foil, fat side up, on rack in uncovered roasting pan.

DO NOT add water.

USE cooking times of *METHOD II*.

The head of the wild boar, extinct in England by the 16th century, was the Christmas dinner of nobleman. The pig became the nearest substitute to the boar.

BASTING LIQUID FOR FOWL

1 cup	dry white Wine	250 mL
1	lemon, juice only	
1/4 cup	rosemary	50 mL
1 tbsp	salt	15 mL

In a bowl, combine all ingredients. Baste fowl.

BASTING LIQUID FOR GOOSE

| 3/4 cup | apricot Brandy | 175 mL |
| | green grapes, seedless | |

The last hour of cooking, drain most fat from roasting pan and baste goose with apricot brandy. The last 15 minutes of cooking, add green grapes to roasting pan. Serve grapes and liquid with dinner over rice.

BASTING LIQUID FOR BEEF

| 2 cups | red Wine | 500 mL |

Baste roast with red Wine. Use for making gravy.

LAMB MARINADE

1/2 cup	oil	125 mL
1/4 cup	wine vinegar (ReaLemon lemon juice from concentrate)	50 mL
1 tsp	salt	5 mL
1 tbsp	parsley	15 mL
2	cloves garlic, crushed	
pinch	oregano	

In a mixing bowl, combine all ingredients and let stand 2 hours. Spread mixture over lamb several hours before cooking.

SAUCE FOR LAMB I

| 1/4-1/2 cup | Crème de Menthe | 50-125 mL |

Remove lamb from oven and place on serving platter. Immediately pour Crème de Menthe over roast.

SAUCE FOR LAMB II

2/3 cup	fresh mint leaves, shredded	150 mL
2 tbsp	sugar	30 mL
1/3 tsp	salt	75 mL
2 cups	white malt vinegar	500 mL

In a saucepan, combine all ingredients and beat well. Strain liquid and use over lamb in place of gravy. Make in large quantities and bottle for gift giving.

SAUCE FOR DUCK

3 tbsp	flour	45 mL
2 tbsp	fat	30 mL
1 cup	stock (boiling water)	250 mL
1/2 cup	orange juice	125 mL
1 tbsp	orange rind, grated	15 mL
1 tbsp	Sherry	15 mL

Remove duck from roasting pan and place pan on burner. Stir in flour and add stock. Add remaining ingredients and continue to stir until thickened. Serve hot, in place of gravy.

PERFECT GRAVY

PROPORTIONS

2 tbsp	fat (from pan drippings)	30 mL
2 tbsp	flour	30 mL
1 cup	liquid (stock, bouillon, liquid reserved from vegetables)	250 mL
	salt, pepper to taste	

Measure fat into roasting pan. Over medium heat, stir flour into fat until smooth. Cook slowly, stirring constantly until mixture bubbles. Slowly add liquid. Continue stirring until gravy thickens and boils one minute. Season to taste with salt and pepper.

"I would be slap-dashing home, the gravy smell of the dinners of others, the bird smell, the brandy, the pudding and mince, weaving up my nostrils . . .
Dylan Thomas, **Conversation About Christmas**

SOLVING GRAVY PROBLEMS

TOO LUMPY run gravy through the blender or food processor and reheat.

TOO PALE add a little black coffee or a few drops of browning sauce.

TOO GREASY add a small amount of baking soda or refrigerate until fat congeals on top and can be skimmed off.

TOO BLAND add a pinch of curry powder to enhance flavour.

HAM GLAZES

FOR BEST RESULTS

GLAZE ham once it is thoroughly cooked. Pre-cooked hams should be glazed after ham is thoroughly heated.

WARMED AND COOKED hams, remove outer casing and rind before glazing.

GLAZE upper surface of ham.

ONCE GLAZED bake, uncovered and without water in pan, at 400 F (200 C) until glaze is set.

GARNISH ham with cherries, pineapples, or peach sections, held in place with toothpicks.

SUGAR GLAZE

1 cup	brown sugar	250 mL
1 tsp	prepared mustard	5 mL
pinch	cloves, ground	
	ginger ale (fruit juice)	

In a mixing bowl, combine sugar, mustard, and cloves. Add enough ginger ale to make a thick paste. Spread on ham and bake until set.

On facing page: **Baked Ham**, page 48, and about **Ham Glazes**, page 52.

APRICOT-NUT GLAZE

1 cup	apricot jam	250 mL
2	egg yolks	
1/2 cup	pecans, ground	125 mL

In a mixing bowl, combine jam and egg yolks and spread on ham. Dust ham with pecans and bake until set.

JAM AND JELLY GLAZES

	dry mustard	
1/2 tsp	gloves, ground (ginger)	2 mL
	peach jam (orange marmalade, red currant jelly)	

Sprinkle ham with dry mustard and ground cloves. Spread on a generous layer of peach jam. Bake until set.

CORN SYRUP GLAZE

2 parts	corn syrup
1 part	crushed pineapple, drained

In a mixing bowl, combine corn syrup and pineapple. Spread on a generous layer of the mixture. Bake until set.

HOT MUSTARD SAUCE
recommended with ham and roast beef

1	egg	
1 tbsp	sugar	15 mL
1/4 tsp	salt	1 mL
3 tbsp	dry mustard	45 mL
1/2 cup	vinegar	125 mL
2 tbsp	butter	30 mL
2 tbsp	vegetable oil	130 mL

In the top part of a double boiler, beat egg and add remaining ingredients, except oil. Stir until thickened. Add oil. Serve hot or cold. Makes about 3/4 cup (175 mL).

HORSERADISH
recommended with roast beef

1/4 cup	horseradish, drained	50 mL
1/2 tsp	salt	2 mL
1 cup	sour cream	250 mL

In a mixing bowl, combine all ingredients. Chill and serve. Makes about 1 cup.

RAW CRANBERRY
recommended with fowl

RAW CRANBERRY		
2 cups	cranberries	500 mL
1	large orange	
3/4 cup	sugar	175 mL

Wash cranberries and orange. Squeeze juice from orange and remove seeds. Grind cranberries and orange through a mincer or with a food processor. Combine raw cranberries and orange with juice and sugar. Refrigerate and serve cold.

CRANBERY MOULD
recommended with fowl

2-3 oz	packages cherry jello	2-85 g
1 cup	boiling water	250 mL
1/2 cup	pineapple juice	125 mL
1 tbsp	ReaLemon juice from concentrate	15 mL
1 cup	sugar	250 mL
1	orange, through mincer	
1 cup	cranberries, through mincer	250 mL
1 cup	celery, finely chopped	250 mL
1 cup	crushed pineapple, drained	250 mL

In a mixing bowl, dissolve gelatin in boiling water and add juice and sugar. Heat until sugar dissolves. Cool and add remaining ingredients. Pour into 2 qt (2 L) mould and refrigerate until firm.

POULTRY SEASONING

2 cups	parsley	500 mL
1 cup	sage	250 mL
1/2 cup	rosemary	125 mL
1/4 cup	marjoram	50 mL
1 tsp	onion powder	5 mL
2 tbsp	salt	30 mL
1 tsp	pepper	5 mL
1/2 tsp	ginger	2 mL

In a mixing bowl, combine all ingredients thoroughly. Package in plastic bags or glass bottles. To use, combine 1 tbsp (15 mL) poultry seasoning with butter and rub on skin of fowl before cooking. Gift giving idea.

STUFFING FACTS

PREPARE stuffing the day or evening before use and refrigerate until use. Stuff fowl or roast just prior to cooking. Use cold stuffing.

DAY old bread is best.

PREPARE 1/2-3/4 cup (125 ml-170 mL) stuffing per lb (500 g) fowl and 1-2 cups (250-500 mL) per lb for other roasts.

ALLOW 2 slices bread per serving
   1 lb (500 g) loaf bread   = 8 cups crumbs (2 L)
   1 lb (500 g) bread crumbs = 1 qt (1 L) dry crumbs
                             = 2 qt (2 L) soft crumbs

PLACE fowl in large mixing bowl to dress.

DO NOT pack stuffing too tighly, otherwise stuffing will swell and be soggy when cooked.

STUFFING may be baked separately in a shallow, uncovered dish for 35 minutes at 350 F (180 C).

REFRIGERATE leftover stuffing, removed from fowl.

WILD FOWL are usually roasted without stuffing, but with sliced apple in the cavity, (discarded and not eaten upon serving).

FARM FRESH chickens are best without stuffing.

Rosemary was the most prized Christmas plant until mid 19th century. Its purple flowers were the symbol of remembrance. The plant was used to flavour and decorate the traditional boar's head dinner.

BREAD STUFFING
recommended for fowl and other roasts

1/4 cup	butter	50 mL
1/2 cup	celery, chopped	125 mL
1/4 cup	onion, chopped	50 mL
4 cups	bread crumbs	1 L
1 tsp	salt	5 mL
pinch	pepper	
1 tsp	sage (poultry seasoning)	5 mL

Sauté celery and onion in butter. In a large bowl, combine all ingredients. 5 cups (1.25 L).

Variations
Add 1/3-1/2 cup (75-125 mL) chopped wlanuts; 1 cup (250 mL) chopped chestnuts; 1/3 lb (165 g) cooked sausage meat; 1/2 pt (250 mL) chopped oysters; 1 cup (250 mL) sauteed mushrooms.

SAUSAGEMEAT STUFFING
recommended for turkey, 10-12 lb (4.5-5.5 kg)

1 1/2 lb	pork sausagemeat	750 g
2 oz	bread crumbs, fresh	60 mL
1/2 tsp	oregano	2 mL
1/2	lemon rind, grated	
	salt, pepper to taste	
	stock (water)	

In a mixing bowl, combine all ingredients using enough stock for stuffing to hold together.

"My dear, I wish for turkey and sausages. It may be weakness, but I own I am partial to sausages."
   Mrs. Gaskell, **Christmas Storms And Sunshine**

CHESTNUT AND OYSTER STUFFING
recommended for turkey, 10-12 lb (5-6 kg)

6 cups	bread cubes, lightly toasted	1.5 L
1	medium onion, chopped	
2 cups	celery, finely chopped	500 mL
2 cups	chestnuts, cooked, dried, chopped	500 mL
8-10	medium oysters, chopped	
1	shredded wheat biscuit, crushed	
1 1/2 tsp	Worcestershire sauce	7 mL
1	clove garlic, mashed	
1 tsp	salt	5 mL
1/2 tsp	poultry seasoning	2 mL
1/4 tsp	thyme	1 mL
1/4 tsp	rosemary	1 mL
1/4 tsp	marjoram	1 mL
1/8 tsp	pepper	O.5 mL
1/2 cup	butter, melted	125 mL

In a mixing bowl, combine all ingredients well. 11 cups (3.75 L).

ALMOND STUFFING
recommended for turkey, 16 lb (8 kg)

2 cups	onion, minced	500 mL
1 lb	butter, melted	500 g
2 cups	celery, chopped	500 mL
1 tsp	thyme	5 mL
1 tsp	marjoram	5 mL
1 tsp	savory	5 mL
1 tsp	sage	5 mL
10 cups	bread crumbs, stale	2.5 L
2 1/2 cups	almonds, slivered, toasted	625 mL

Sauté onion in a portion of the butter. In a mixing bowl, combine all ingredients well. 16 cups (4 L).

"My God, what masses of food here, turkey, large tongues, long wall of roast loin of pork, pork-pies, sausages, mince-pies, dark cakes covered with almonds, cheese-cakes, lemon-tarts, jellies, endless masses of food, with whiskey, gin, port wine, burgundy, muscatel. It seems incredible."
D.H. Lawrence, **The Selected Letters Of D.H. Lawrence.**

PECAN STUFFING
recommended for chicken, 5-6 lb (2.5-3 kg)

1/2 cup	onion, minced	125 mL
1 cup	butter	250 mL
4 cups	bread crumbs, dry	1 L
1 cup	pecans, chopped	250 mL
pinch	salt	
	light cream or dry white wine	

Sauté onion in butter. In a mixing bowl, combine all ingredients well using enough cream for stuffing to hold together.

APPLE-PRUNE STUFFING
recommended for goose, 12 lb (6 kg)

1	large onion, finely chopped	
3 cups	apples, peeled, chopped	750 mL
2 cups	prunes, pitted, finely chopped	500 mL
5 cups	bread crumbs	1.25 L
1/2 tsp	salt	2 mL
1/2 tsp	nutmeg	2 mL
2 tbsp	butter	30 mL
	ReaLemon lemon juice from concentrate	

In a mixing bowl, combine all ingredients well using enough ReaLemon for stuffing to hold together. 12 cups (3 L).

FRUIT STUFFING
recommended for goose, 12 lb (6 kg)

2 1/2 cups	prunes, pitted	625 mL
1/3 cup	Sherry (water)	75 mL
2 1/2 cups	cooking apples, peeled, shredded	625 mL
2 1/2 cups	raisins	625 mL
2 1/2 cups	apricots, dried	625 mL
1 cup	bread crumbs, fresh	250 mL
1/2 tsp	ginger	2 mL
1/2 tsp	cinnamon	2 mL
1/4 tsp	nutmeg	1 mL
8	cloves	

Soak prunes overnight in Sherry or water and chop fine. In a mixing bowl, combine all ingredients well, including Sherry. To increase or decrease quantity, keep portions of fruit equal. 12 cups (3 L).

APPLE-RAISIN STUFFING
recommended for goose, 12 lb (6 kg)

1 cup	onion, chopped	250 mL
1	goose liver, chopped	
1/2 cup	butter	125 mL
4 cups	bread crumbs	1 L
4 cups	apples, peeled, chopped	1 L
1 cup	raisins	250 mL
1/2 tsp	salt	2 mL
1/2 tsp	pepper	2 mL
1/2 tsp	mace	2 mL
1/2 tsp	nutmeg	2 mL
2 tbs	poultry seasoning	30 mL
1/4 cup	parsley, chopped	50 mL

Sauté onions and liver in butter; add bread crumbs and brown. In a mixing bowl, combine all ingredients well. 10 cups (2.5 L).

SAGE AND ONION STUFFING
recommended for goose, duck, 4-5 lb (2-2.5 kg)

3	large onions, parboiled, chopped	
3 1/2 cups	bread crumbs, dry	875 mL
1/2 cup	raisins	125 mL
1 tsp	salt	5 mL
1/2 tsp	pepper	2 mL
1 tbsp	sage	15 mL
1 tbsp	butter	15 mL

In a mixing bowl, combine all ingredients well. 4 cups (1 L).

SAUERKRAUT STUFFING
recommended for duck 4-5 lb (2-2.25 kg)

4 cups	sauerkraut	1 L
1	medium onion, chopped	
2 tbsp	butter	30 mL
1	small tart apple, peeled, chopped	
1 tbsp	caraway seeds	15 mL

Drain and rinse sauerkraut in hot water. Sauté onion in butter. In a mixing bowl, combine all ingredients well. 4 cups (1 L).

MINT STUFFING
recommended for lamb, 5-6 lb (2.5-3 kg)

1/4 cup	celery, chopped	50 mL
2 tbsp	onion, chopped	30 mL
6 tbsp	butter	90 mL
3 cups	bread crumbs, soft	750 mL
1	egg	
2 tbsp	water	30 mL
1/3 cup	mint, chopped	75 mL
1/2 tsp	poultry seasoning (sage)	2 mL
1/2 tsp	marjoram	2 mL
1/2 tsp	thyme	2 mL
pinch	salt, pepper	

Sauté celery and onion in butter and add crumbs. In a mixing bowl, beat egg and water and add crumb mixture. Combine thoroughly and add spices, salt and pepper. Lightly pack centre of roast.

PINEAPPLE-GINGER STUFFING
recommended for lamb, 5-6 lb (2.5-3 kg)

2 1/4 cups	bread crumbs	550 mL
2 cups	crushed pineapple, drained	500 mL
3/4 cup	brown sugar	175 mL
1	large onion, chopped	
4 tbsp	ReaLemon lemon juice from concentrate	60 mL
1/2 cup	walnuts	125 mL
4 tbsp	butter	60 mL
1 1/4 tsp	ginger	6 mL
1	garlic clove, crushed	
	ReaLemon lemon juice from concentrate	

Sauté bread crumbs in butter until browned. Remove from heat and stir in remaining ingredients. Brush inside of roast with ReaLemon. Lightly pack center of roast.

"We had our Christmas dinner at five: dehydrated potatoes and onions and a bit of moose steak, especially saved and tendered, baked in a pan with stuffing. For dessert there were jam tarts and chocolate cake."
Theodora C. Stanwell-Fletcher, **Frostbound 1937**

VEGETABLE	1 LB EQUIVALENT	AMOUNT PER SERVING
asparagus	10-12 stocks	1/3 lb (170 g)
green beans		1/4 lb (125 g)
beets		1/3 lb (170 g)
broccoli		1/3 lb (170 g)
brussels sprouts		1/3 lb (170 g)
cabbage	6 cups shredded	1/6 lb (85 g)
carrots	3 1/2 cups (875 mL) raw, chopped	1/4 lb (125 g)
	4 cups (1 L) raw, shredded	
cauliflower		1/3 lb (170 g)
celery	4 cups (1 L)	
cucumber	1 average = 1 1/3 cups (325 mL), diced	
eggplant		1/3 lb (170 g)
mushrooms	5 3/4 cups (1.5 L), sliced	
onions	3 cups (750 mL), chopped	1/4 lb (125 g)
	4 cups (1 L), sliced	
parsnips		1/4 lb (125 g)
peas	3 cups (750 mL)	1/2 lb (250 g)
potatoes	3-4, peeled	1/3 lb (170 g)
	4 cups (1 L), diced, raw	
	3 cups (750 mL), diced, cooked	
	2 cups (500 mL), mashed, cooked	
rice	2 1/4-2 1/2 cups (550-625 mL) raw	
	6-8 cups, cooked	
spinach		1/2 lb (250 g)
squash (hubbard)		1/2 lb (250 g)
turnips		1/4 lb (125 g)
yams		1/3 lb (170 g)
zucchini		1/2 lb (250 g)

YORKSHIRE PUDDING

1 cup	flour	250 mL
1/2 tsp	salt	2 mL
3	eggs	
1 cup	milk	250 mL
1 tbsp	parsley	15 mL
1/4 tsp	rosemary	1 mL
1/4 tsp	thyme	1 mL
	beef drippings	

Sift flour and salt. In a mixing bowl, beat eggs with milk and gradually add flour and spices. Beat until smooth and refrigerate 20 minutes. Pour 1 1/2 tbsp (22 mL) beef drippings into each muffin tin or 1/2 cup (125 mL) into an 8'' (2 L) square pan. Pour batter to a depth of 3/4'' (1.75 cm) and bake 15 minutes at 450 F (230 C). Reduce heat to 350 F (180 C) and bake 10-15 minutes more, until pudding is puffy and browned. 6-8 servings.

SAUCES FOR VEGETABLES

BASIC WHITE SAUCE (BÉCHAMEL SAUCE)

2 tbsps	butter	30 mL
2 tbsps	flour	30 mL
2 cups	milk	500 mL
	salt, white pepper	
	nutmeg, grated (optional)	
	heavy cream (optional)	

In a saucepan, melt butter. Stir in flour and cook over low heat for 5 minutes. Add all the milk at once and whisk continually. Season with salt, then simmer for 30 minutes stirring occasionally. Once sauce has thickened, add pepper and nutmeg. Add cream for a whiter, richer sauce. Makes about 1 1/2 cups (375 mL).

CHEESE SAUCE

2 tbsps	butter	30 mL
2 tbsps	flour	30 mL
1 cup	milk	250 mL
	salt, white pepper	
1/2 cup	Cheddar cheese, grated	125 mL
1/2 tsp	Dijon mustard	2 ml
	nutmeg (optional)	

In a saucepan, melt butter. Remove from heat and stir in flour and blend well. Add milk in small quantities and blend together. Return to heat and bring almost to a boil stirring continuously. Add seasonings, then cheese and mustard. Simmer 2 minutes. Makes about 1 cup (250 mL).

MORNAY SAUCE

2 tbsps	butter	30 mL
2 tbsps	flour	30 mL
1 cup	milk	250 mL
1	egg yolk	
2 tbsps	cream	30 mL
2 tbsps	Parmesan cheese, grated	30 mL
1/4 cup	Gruyere cheese	50 mL

In a saucepan, melt butter. Stir in flour and cook over low heat for 3 minutes. Slowly add milk and stir constantly. Continue to cook until thick. In a mixing bowl, beat egg and cream. Add some sauce to egg mixture, stirring constantly.Return egg mixture to sauce and heat thoroughly. Add cheese and stir until melted and blended. Makes about 1 cup (250 mL).

PAN ROASTED POTATOES

Parboil potatoes for approximately 15 minutes. Place around roast for 45 minutes. When roast is removed from oven, place potatoes in a shallow pan and broil for several minutes or until brown.

"Master Peter Cratchit plunged a fork into the saucepan of potatoes . . ."
Charles Dickens, A Christmas Carol

IRRISISTABLE CREAMY POTATOES

9	large potatoes	
1-8 oz	package cream cheese	250 g
1 cup	sour cream	250 mL
2 tsps	onion salt	10 mL
1 tsp	salt	5 mL
pinch	pepper	
1 tbsp	butter	30 mL

Cook and mash potatoes until very smooth. Add remaining ingredients, except butter. Place in a large buttered casserole dish and dot with butter. Bake covered for 30 minutes at 350 F (180 C). Can be made ahead and frozen. Thaw before baking if frozen. 10-12 servings.

CHESTNUTS

chestnuts
water (chicken stock)
salt
butter
salt, pepper to taste

Wash and cut a slit in the shell of each chestnut. In a saucepan, boil chestnuts for 15-20 minutes. Remove shells and inner skins while still hot. Stew chestnuts in salted water or chicken stock for 15 minutes until tender. Drain well. Serve hot with butter, salt, and pepper to taste.

CHESTNUTS WITH BRUSSELS SPROUTS

12 ozs	chestnuts	365 g
1 lb	brussels sprouts	1 kg
1/2 cup	butter	125 mL
	butter, salt, pepper to taste	

Prepare chestnuts as above, however, instead of stewing, fry chestnuts for 5 minutes in melted butter. Remove outer leaves and stalks from brussels sprouts and cut a cross in the bases. Cook in boiling water for 15 minutes. Drain. Toss with chestnuts. Serve hot with butter, salt, and pepper to taste. 6-8 servings.

"Eked out by applesauce and mashed potatoes, it was a sufficient dinner for the whole family . . ." Charles Dickens, **A Christmas Carol**

CELERY CASSEROLE

4 cups	celery, cut in 1/2″ (1.5 cm) pieces	1 L
3/4 cup	blanched almonds, halved (optional)	175 mL
2 tbsps	butter	30 mL
2 tbsps	flour	30 mL
1-10 oz	can cream of chicken soup	284 mL
1/2 cup	milk	125 mL
1	egg, beaten	
3/4 cup	bread crumbs, buttered	175 mL

Cook celery until almost tender and drain. In a casserole dish, place celery and almonds. In a saucepan, melt butter and blend in flour, soup and milk. Cook until thickened. Remove from heat and quickly stir in beaten egg. Pour mixture over celery and blend thoroughly. Top with buttered bread crumbs and bake 45 minutes at 300 F (150 C). 8 servings.

CAULIFLOWER LOAF

1 tbsp	butter	15 mL
2-10 oz	packages frozen cauliflower	2-300 g
1 cup	Béchamel sauce	250 mL
3	eggs, beaten	
	salt, pepper to taste	
2 tbsps	dry Sherry	30 mL
1 cup	Mornay sauce	250 mL

In a frying pan, melt butter and add frozen cauliflower. Cover and cook about 5 minutes on low heat, until tender. In a blender or food processor, puree the cauliflower. Combine with Béchmel sauce. Add remaining ingredients, except Mornay sauce. Place in a greased loaf pan and bake 30 minutes at 375 F (190 C). Unmould loaf on a serving dish and cover with Mornay sauce. 6-8 servings.

" . . . the warm heavy smell of turkey and ham and celery rose from the plates . . ."
James Joyce, **A Portrait Of The Artist As A Young Man**

BROCCOLI CASSEROLE

1/2 cup	water	125 mL
1/2 tsp	sugar	2 mL
1 1/2 lbs	broccoli	750 g
1 cup	Mornay sauce	250 mL
1 1/2 cups	bread cubes	375 mL
1/4 cup	butter, melted	50 mL

Trim broccoli leaving stems 2 1/2-3" (6.25-7.5 cm) in length. Bring water to a boil. Add sugar and broccoli and cook until broccoli is tender-crisp. Drain. Place broccoli in a buttered casserole dish. Pour Mornay sauce over broccoli. Combine bread cubes and melted butter and sprinkle on top of casserole. Bake for 15 minutes at 350 F (180 C), or until bubbly. 6-8 servings.

SCALLOPED PEAS AND ONIONS

2 tbsps	butter	30 mL
2 cups	onions, sliced	500 mL
1-10 oz	can cream of celery soup	284 mL
1/4 cup	milk	50 mL
1/4 tsp	salt	1 mL
1/8 tsp	pepper	0.5 mL
1/2 tsp	savory	2 mL
1 tbsp	parsley, chopped	15 mL
1-12 oz	package frozen peas	340 mL
1/4 cup	bread crumbs, fine, dry	50 mL
1 tbsp	butter, melted	15 mL

In a saucepan, melt butter. Add onion and cook slowly until onion is limp. Add soup, milk, and seasonings. In a buttered casserole dish, spread frozen peas. Pour soup mixture over peas. Toss bread crumbs and melted butter and sprinkle over soup mixture. Bake for 30 minutes at 350 F (180 C), until peas are tender.

Champlain's Christmas celebration at Saint Croix in Nova Scotia is one of the earliest recorded celebrations of the 17th Century. The feast consisted of numerous courses: corn bread cakes; eel, salmon and beans boiled together; meat soup with nuts; corn, peas and squash; roast venison and squirel pie; wild pigeons, partridges, blackbirds and owls; and for desert, maple sugar cakes and sweetmeat of nuts and sunflower seeds served with a sauce of dried berries and boiling water.

EGGPLANT CASSEROLE

1	medium eggplant	
1 slice	bread	
1/4 cup	milk	50 mL
1	egg	
1/2 lb	Cheddar cheese, grated	250 g
	salt, pepper, to taste	
	bread crumbs, buttered	
	Cheddar cheese, grated	

Peel, cube and boil eggplant until tender. Drain and set aside. In a mixing bowl, soak bread in milk and beat in egg. Mix in cheese and hot eggplant. Place in a buttered casserole dish and bake 45 minutes at 325 F (160 C). Serve hot. May be prepared 1 day before serving. 4-6 servings.

WILD RICE

1 cup	wild rice	250 mL
5 cups	cold water (chicken stock	1.25 L
1 1/2 tsps	salt	7 mL
2 tbsps	butter	30 mL
	pepper to taste	

Wash rice. In a saucepan, place rice, water and salt. Cover and bring slowly to a boil. Stir to separate rice grains. Boil, without stirring, 30–40 minutes. Drain. Rice should be well opened. Place rice in a casserole dish with butter and pepper. Bake for 10-15 minutes at 325 F (160 C). For a variation, sautéed onions and mushrooms may be added to rice before placing in the oven. Serve hot. 4-6 servings.

The first Canadian Christmas was observed in 1535 by Jacques Cartier and his men on the banks of the Ste. Crois River (now the St. Charles) near Quebec City. Supplies were low and many of the 110 men were beginning to suffer from scurvey. They dined on salt, meat, and stale vegetables.

BRUSSELS SPROUTS WITH ONION BUTTER

1	medium onion, sliced	
3 tbsps	butter	45 mL
2 lbs	brussels sprouts	1 kg
1/2 cup	chicken stock	125 mL
	salt, pepper to taste	

Sauté onion in butter until golden brown. Cook brussels sprouts in chicken stock until tender and drain. Pour onion butter over sprouts and season to taste. 6 servings.

GREEN BEANS WITH GREEN ONIONS

2 lbs	green beans	1 kg
1/2 cup	green onions, chopped	125 mL
1 tbsp	butter	15 mL
	salt, pepper, to taste	

Sauté onion in butter. Cook beans until tender and drain. Pour onion butter over beans and season to taste. 6-8 servings.

CANDIED CARROTS

1-14 oz	can carrots, small, whole	398 mL
1 tbsp	butter	15 mL
2 tbsps	brown sugar	30 mL
1 tsp	ReaLemon lemon juice from concentrate	5 mL
	nutmeg	

In a saucepan, heat carrots until hot and drain. In a different saucepan, melt butter and add brown sugar and lemon. Stir until thickened and add carrots. Continue heating until thickened. Heat carrots until coated with syrup. Serve hot, sprinkled with nutmeg. 4 servings.

On facing page: **Candied Carrots** (bottom), page 70, **Lime Jello Mould** (top right), page 87, and **Raw Cranberry** (left), page 56.

GINGERED CARROTS

1 lb	carrots, peeled, chopped	500 g
2 tbsps	butter	30 mL
1/2 tbsp	candied ginger, minced (grated ginger)	7 mL

Cook carrots until tender and drain. In a saucepan, melt butter and add ginger and carrots. Heat until carrots are lightly browned. 4 servings.

CAROL'S LEMON CARROTS

24	small carrots, cut on an angle	
1/2 cup	butter	125 mL
1/2 cup	white sugar	125 mL
2 tsps	lemon rind	10 mL
1 tbsp	ReaLemon lemon juice from concentrate	15 mL

Cook carrots until tender-crisp and drain. In a saucepan, melt butter and stir in sugar until it dissolves. Add lemon rind and ReaLemon. Place carrots in a casserole dish. Pour butter mixture over carrots. Bake uncovered for 20 minutes at 350 F (180 C). 4 servings.

SWEET POTATOES IN ORANGE CUPS

1-19 oz	can sweet potatoes	540 mL
1 tbsp	butter	15 mL
1/4 tsp	nutmeg	1 ml
	salt, pepper to taste	
3	oranges	
6	marshmallows	

Drain sweet potatoes and mash in a bowl. Mix in butter, nutmeg and season to taste. Cut oranges in half. Squeeze juice of each half and flatten pulp to form a cup. Fill each cup with sweet potato mixture. Top each with a marshmallow and bake for 20 minutes at 350 F (18o C). Brown marshmallow under broiler if desired. 6 servings.

"Mr. Edwards was taking sweet potatoes out of his pockets. He said they had helped to balance the package on his head when he swam across the creek. He thought Pa and Ma might like them, with the Christmas turkey."
Laura Ingles Wilder, **Christmas On The Prairie**

Christmas Buffet

SHRIMP CURRIED EGGS

12	eggs, hard-boiled, halved, with the yolks removed	
1/3 cup	mayonnaise	75 mL
1/2 tsp	salt	2 mL
1/4 tsp	dry mustard	1 mL
1/2 tsp	curry powder	2 mL
1/2 tsp	paprika	2 mL
2 tbsp	butter	30 mL
2 tbsp	flour	30 mL
10 oz	milk	300 mL
1-10 oz	can cream of shrimp soup	284 mL
1/2 cup	sharp Cheddar cheese, grated	125 mL
2-4 oz	cans of shrimp	2-113 g
2 tbsp	butter	30 mL
1 cup	bread crumbs	250 mL

In a bowl, mash egg yolks, mayonnaise, salt, mustard, curry powder and paprika. Return mixture to egg halves and place in a large, flat casserole. In a saucepan, melt butter and stir in flour. Add milk and soup, heating until combined. Add cheese and stir until cheese is melted and sauce is thick. Fold in shrimps. Pour mixture over eggs. In a saucepan, melt butter and add bread crumbs. Mix until crumbs are coated. Place bread crumbs around the edges of the casserole. Bake for 15-20 minutes, or until bubbly, at 350 F (180 C).

CREPES

1 1/2 cups	milk	375 mL
3	eggs	
2 tbsp	butter, melted	30 mL
1 cup	flour	250 mL
1/2 tsp	salt	2 mL

Combine all ingredients in a blender or food processor for 1 minute. Lightly grease a 6'' (15 cm) skillet. Spoon enough batter onto pan to cover bottom. Rotate pan so batter is thin. Cook crepes quickly over high heat, and turn to cook other side. Grease pan with each crepe.

SALMON FILLING FOR CREPES

1/4 cup	butter	50 mL
1/4 cup	flour	50 mL
1 tsp	tarragon	5 mL
1/4 tsp	salt, pepper	1 mL
1 cup	cream	250 mL
2	egg yolks, slightly beaten	
1-7.5 oz	can salmon, drained	213 g
2 tbsp	chopped chives	30 mL
2 1/2 tbsp	white Wine	12 mL
1/4 cup	Parmesan cheese, grated	50 mL

In a saucepan, melt butter and stir in flour until well blended. Add tarragon, salt and pepper. Stirring constantly, gradually add cream and cook until sauce thickens. In a separate bowl, stir half the sauce into the egg yolks. Pour this mixture back into the saucepan and cook 1 minute. Using 3/4 of the sauce mixture, blend with the salmon. Divide mixture among crepes and roll each crepe. Place crepes in a buttered casserole dish, seam side down. Add wine to remaining sauce and pour over crepes. Top with Parmesan cheese and bake 10 minutes, until bubbly, at 350 F (180 C). 6 servings.

NANCY'S MANICOTTI

8	manicotti shells	
1/2 cup	onions, finely chopped	125 mL
2 tbsp	cooking oil	30 mL
2 cups	cooked ham, ground or chopped	500 mL
1 cup	mushrooms, sliced	250 mL
3 tbsp	Parmesan cheese, grated	45 mL
1/4 cup	green pepper, chopped	50 mL
3 tbsp	butter	45 mL
3 tbsp	flour	45 mL
2 cups	milk	500 mL
6 oz	Swiss cheese, grated	188 g

Cook manicotti shells according to instructions on package. Cool and set aside. In a large frying pan, brown onion in oil. Add ham and mushrooms and sauté. Place in a bowl to cool. Add Parmesan cheese and stir well. In the same frying pan, sauté green peppers in butter until tender. Sprinkle with flour and mix well. Remove from heat and add milk all at once. Return to heat and stir constantly until mixture is thick and bubbly. Stir in 3/4 of cheese. Remove from heat once the cheese is blended. Add remaining cheese to ham mixture. Spoon the ham mixture into indivudual manicotti shells. Arrange manicotti shells in a buttered 13 x 9 x 2" (3.5 L) baking dish. Pour cheese sauce over manicotti and sprinkle with paprika. Bake covered for 30 minutes at 375 F (190 C). Remove cover and bake another 10 minutes. 4 servings.

MEATBALLS

2 lb	ground beef	1 kg
1 1/2 cups	soft bread crumbs (3 slices of bread)	375 mL
1/2 cup	milk	125 mL
1/4 cup	onion, finely chopped	50 mL
2	eggs	
1 1/2 tsp	salt	7 mL

In a mixing bowl, combine all ingredients. Form into bite-sized balls. Place on an ungreased cookie sheet and bake at 375 F (190 C) for 25–30 minutes. Makes approximately 4 dozen balls.

MEATBALL SAUCE

2 tbsp	onion, minced	30 mL
2 tbsp	green pepper, chopped	30 mL
1 tbsp	vegetable oil	15 mL
1 cup	tomatoes, skinned & chopped	250 mL
1-10 oz	can chopped mushrooms, drained	284 mL
1 tsp	brown sugar	5 mL
1/4 tsp	dried oregano	1 mL
1/4 tsp	dried basil	1 mL
1/4 tsp	garlic, minced	1 mL

In a skillet, brown the onion and green pepper in oil. Add remaining ingredients and simmer 20 minutes. Serve with meatballs.

BEEF STROGANOFF

4 lbs	round steak, sliced 1/8″ (2.5 mm) thick)	2 kg
2 cups	onions, sliced	500 mL
1/2 cup	butter	125 mL
1 lb	mushrooms, sliced	500 g
1 cup	bouillon (substitute half with dry white wine)	250 mL
3 cups	sour cream	750 mL
	salt, pepper, prepared mustard to taste	

Pound the steak until thin, then cut in pieces approximately 3'' (8 cm) long. Cook onion slices in butter until wilted. Add mushrooms and beef and simmer for 5 minutes. Pour in bouillon and cover. Simmer for 45 minutes, until meat is tender and the liquid has almost evaporated. Stir in sour cream and season to taste with salt, pepper and mustard. Keep hot until serving. DO NOT BOIL. 12 servings.

SHIRLEY'S PORK TENDERLOIN CASSEROLE

2	8" (20 cm) tenderloin rolls	
1	medium onion, finely chopped	
2 tbsp	butter	30 mL
1/2 lb	mushrooms, sliced	125 g
	flour	
1-10 oz	can mushroom soup	284 mL
4 oz	water	125 mL
4 oz	sour cream	125 mL

Cut each tenderloin into 6 pieces and pound thin. In a frying pan sauté onion in butter. Add mushrooms and brown. Then remove onions and mushrooms from pan and set aside in a bowl. Flour tenderloin and brown on both sides in the same frying pan. Place tenderloin pieces in a greased casserole dish. Tenderloin may be layered or spread out, depending upon the size of the dish. Sprinkle meat with mushrooms and onions. In a bowl, combine mushroom soup, water and sour cream. Pour over tenderloin and bake for 1 1/2 hours at 350 F (180 C). 4-6 servings.

BARBECUED SHORT RIBS

2 lb	short ribs	1 kg
1 tbsp	butter	15 mL
1/2 cup	onions, finely chopped	125 mL
1/2 tsp	pepper	2 mL
4 tsp	sugar	20 mL
1 tsp	dry mustard	5 mL
1 tsp	paprika	5 mL
4 tsp	Worcesterchire sauce	20 mL
1 tsp	Tobasco sauce	5 mL
1/2 cup	ketchup	125 mL
1/4 cup	vinegar	50 mL
1/4 cup	water	50 mL

In a frying pan, melt butter and sauté onions until clear. Add dry seasonings, sauces, vinegar, and water and bring to a boil. Cut ribs into serving size pieces and brown in a heavy skillet. Place ribs in a large casserole dish, ribs pointing up, and cover with sauce. Cover and bake 1 1/2 hours at 350 F (180 C). Remove cover and baste. Bake uncovered for 15 minutes or until tender. 4-6 servings.

The name "Santa Claus" is taken from the Dutch name "Sinterklaus".

BARBECUED SPARE RIBS

2 lb	spare ribs	1 kg
2	onions, finely chopped	
2 tbsp	butter	30 mL
1/4 cup	brown sugar	50 mL
1 tsp	dry mustard	5 mL
1/2 cup	vinegar	125 mL
1/2 cup	chilli sauce	125 mL
2 tbsp	ReaLemon lemon juice from concentrate	30 mL
2 tbsp	Worcestershire sauce	30 mL
2-3	whole cloves	
	garlic salt to taste	

In a large frying pan, sauté onions in butter until tender. In a mixing bowl, combine all ingredients. Add to the onions and simmer 15 minutes. Place the ribs, rib side up in a 13 x 9 x 2'' (3 L) pan. Cover ribs with half the sauce. Cook covered for 1 1/2 hours at 350 F (180 C). Baste frequently until remaining sauce is utilized. Bake uncovered the last 10 minutes. 4-6 servings.

HARRY'S SHRIMP CASSEROLE

1	medium onion, finely chopped	
2 tbsp	butter	30 mL
1/2 lb	mushrooms, sliced	250 g
1 1/2 cups	canned tomatoes	375 mL
1/2 cup	light cream	125 mL
2 tbsp	flour	30 mL
1/4 cup	dry Sherry	50 mL
1 lb	fresh raw shrimps	500 g
1 tsp	Worcestershire sauce	5 mL
1/4 tsp	paprika	1 mL
1/4 tsp	thyme	1 mL
	salt, pepper to taste	
1/2 cup	dry bread crumbs	125 mL
1/4 cup	Parmesan cheese, grated	50 mL
2 tbsp	butter, melted	30 mL

In a large pot, simmer onions and butter until golden. Add mushrooms and continue to simmer one minute. Add tomatoes and simmer 10 minutes. Stir in cream, then sprinkle flour on top. Continue to stir until flour dissolves. Add Sherry, shrimps, and seasonings. Pour into a casserole dish. In a separate bowl, combine bread crumbs, cheese and butter. Sprinkle on top of casserole. Bake for 20 minutes at 400 F (200 C). 4-6 servings.

Befana is the Italian female counterpart of Santa Claus. On Epiphany or Twelfth Night, she fills children's stockings with presents.

SUPER SEAFOOD CASSEROLE

3 cups	milk and cream mixture	750 mL
1/3 cup	butter	75 mL
6 tbsp	flour	90 mL
	salt, pepper to taste	
pinch	cayenne pepper	
1 tsp	Worcestershire sauce	5 mL
	OR	
2 tbsp	dry Sherry (Madeira)	30 ml
1 lb	shrimp, cooked	500 g
7 oz	frozen crabmeat, thawed and flaked	200 g
2	large filets of haddock, steamed	
	Parmesan cheese, grated	
	OR	
	Cheddar cheese, grated	

In the top part of a double boiler, scald milk/cream mixture. In a saucepan, melt butter. Blend in flour and spices. Slowly stir in hot cream mixture and return to double boiler. Cook, stirring frequently until sauce thickens. Remove from heat and add Worcestershire sauce or Sherry. Fold in cooked shrimps, flaked crabmeat, and flaked haddock. Place in a well-greased baking dish and sprinkle with cheese. Bake approximately 30 minutes, until bubbly and cheese has browned, at 375 F (190 C). May be made the day before serving and chilled overnight. 6 servings as main course. 12 servings as buffet course.

CRAB AND TUNA CASSEROLE

1-6 oz	can crab meat	170 g
1-4 1/2 oz	can tuna	120 g
5 cups	fresh bread cubes	1.25 L
8 oz	cheese, cubed	250 g
2 tbsp	chopped parsley	30 mL
4	eggs	
3 cups	milk	750 mL
1/2 tsp	salt	2 mL
1/8 tsp	pepper	0.5 mL
2 tsp	dry mustard	10 mL
1/4 tsp	onion powder	1 mL
3 tbsp	butter, melted	45 mL

Drain crab and tuna and flake into a mixing bowl. Stir until combined. Place 1/3 of the bread cubes in a buttered casserole dish. Layer 1/3 of the crab and tuna on top. Top with 1/3 of the cheese cubes, and 1/3 of the parsley. Repeat layers two more times. In a separate bowl, beat eggs, milk, seasonings, and butter until well blended. Pour over layers in casserole. Cover and refrigerate overnight. Then bake at 350 F (180 C), uncovered for 1 hour and 15 minutes.

UNCLE WALTER'S NEW YORK CHICKEN CACCIATORE

8	chicken pieces	
16	onions, small, whole	
16	carrots, cut in sticks	
16	potatoes, small or 4 large ones, quartered	
1 tsp	basil	5 mL
1/4 tsp	curry powder	1 mL
1 tsp	sage	5 mL
1 tsp	thyme	5 mL
1 tsp	savoury	5 mL
1 tsp	rosemary	5 mL
	water	
1 qt	homogenized milk	1 L
1 cup	evaporated milk	250 mL
2-10 oz	cans mushrooms soup	2-284 mL
1/2 tsp	garlic powder	2 mL

In a large pot, place chicken and vegetables. Sprinkle with spices and add just enough water for simmering. Cook covered until carrots are almost done. Add milk and mushroom soup and continue to simmer. Sprinkle with garlic powder. 6-8 servings.

CHICKEN A LA KING

1/4 lb	fresh mushrooms, sliced	125 g
1/2 cup	green pepper, chopped	125 mL
2	pimentos, chopped	
1/4 cup	butter, melted	50 mL
3 tbsp	flour	5 mL
1 cup	chicken bouillon	250 mL
1/2 cup	milk	125 mL
	salt, pepper, to taste	
1/4 tsp	tumeric	1 mL
1 tsp	sugar	5 mL
1/2 cup	heavy cream	125 mL
2	egg yolks, slightly beaten	
2 cups	cooked chicken (turkey),cubed	500 mL
1-10 oz	mushroom soup	284 mL

In a frying pan, sauté mushrooms, green peppers, and pimentos in butter. Remove from heat and stir in flour. Blend in chicken bouillon and milk and add salt, pepper, tumeric and sugar. Cook slowly over low heat until mixture thickens. In a mixing bowl, combine heavy cream and egg yolks. Add to bouillon mixture and blend thoroughly. Fold in chicken and continue heating until chicken is hot. Serve over patty shells. 6-8 servings. As an appetizer, fill pastry bouchées.

MARY'S CHICKEN LASAGNA

	lasagna noodles for 2 layers of a lasagna pan comercial spaghetti sauce	
2 tsp	basil	10 mL
2 tsp	oregano	10 mL
4 tbsp	butter	60 mL
1 lb	mushrooms	500 g
2	medium onions, chopped	
2 lb	chicken or turkey breast, cooked and thinly sliced	1 kg
1 tbsp	tarragon	15 mL
2 cups	Mozzarella cheese, shredded	500 mL
1-12 oz	can asparagus tips (not fresh or frozen), drained	341 mL
	Parmesan cheese, grated	

Cook lasagna noodles according to instructions on package. Run noodles under cold water and set aside. Cover the bottom of a lasagna pan with spaghetti sauce. Add 1 tsp. (5 mL) of basil and oregano to sauce and cover with first layer of lasagna noodles. In a frying pan, melt butter and sauté mushrooms and onions. Place thin slices of chicken on first layer of lasagna noodles. Sprinkle chicken with tarragon. Add mushrooms and onions to layer of chicken. Cover with 1 cup (250 mL) of Mozzarella cheese. Cover cheese with asparagus tips. Top with second layer of lasagna noodles. Smooth a generous layer of spaghetti sauce over noodles. Cover with remaining Mozzarella cheese. Top with grated Parmesan cheese. Bake for 30 minutes, until bubbly and cheese has browned, at 350 F (180 C). 6 servings.

HELEN'S FABULOUS CHICKEN PIE

6 tbsp	butter, melted	90 mL
1 1/2 cups	celery, diced	375 mL
1 cup	onion, minced	250 mL
6 tbsp	flour	90 mL
1-10 oz	can mushroom soup	284 mL
3 cups	milk	750 mL
1/4 tsp	dry basil	1 mL
2 tbsp	pimento	30 mL
3 tbsp	dry Sherry	45 mL
4 cups	cooked chicken, diced	1 L
	salt, pepper to taste	
1/2 cup	Cheddar cheese, grated	125 mL
2	unbaked pie shells with tops	

In a large electric frying pan, sauté celery and onions in melted butter. Sift flour over onions and celery and stir. In a blender combine soup and milk. Add basil, pimento, and Sherry and stir by hand. Fold in chicken. Add this mixture to onions and celery and heat until thick and creamy. Add salt and pepper to taste. Fill pie shell. Sprinkled with grated cheese. Place pastry top on and bake for approximately 30 minutes, or until pastry is brown, at 350 F (180 C). Makes 2 pies. Recipe can be used in a deep dish casserole with pie crust only on the top.

CHICKEN ALMANDINE

2 tbsp	butter	30 mL
1 cup	uncooked rice	250 mL
2 cups	mushrooms, sliced	500 mL
1/2 cup	almonds, blanched, slivered	125 mL
1	onion, finely chopped	
1/2	green pepper, finely chopped	
2 cups	hot water	500 mL
1/2 tsp	salt	2 mL
2 cups	cooked chicken	500 mL
1-10 oz	can mushroom soup	284 mL
8 oz	sour cream	250 mL
	parsley	
	toasted almonds	

In a large electric frying pan, melt butter and stir in rice, mushrooms, almonds, onion, and green pepper. Cook until lightly brown, stirring frequently. Stir in water and salt and bring to a boil. Cover and reduce heat, simmering for 15 minutes. Stir occasionally. When rice is tender, add chicken, mushroom soup and sour cream. Heat thoroughly. DO NOT BOIL. Transfer to a casserole dish for serving and keeping warm in the oven. Garnish with parsley and toasted almonds before serving. 6-8 servings.

Christmas day, 1901, the Commonwealth of Australia was proclaimed.

CHICKEN CASHEW CASSEROLE

2 cups	cooked chicken, diced	500 mL
1-10 oz	can mushroom soup	284 mL
1/2 cup	cashew nuts, whole or pieces	125 mL
1/4 cup	onion, finely chopped	50 mL
1/4 cup	celery, chopped	50 mL
1 tsp	salt	5 mL
1/4 tsp	pepper	1 mL
	cashew nuts, whole	

In a mixing bowl, combine all ingredients except whole cashew nuts. Place in a lightly buttered 2 qt (2 L) casserole dish. Cover and cook 30 minutes at 350 F (180 C). Garnish with whole cashew nuts before serving. 6-8 servings.

CHINESE CASSEROLE

1 1/2-2 cups	cooked chicken, diced	375-500 mL
1-10 oz	can mushroom soup	284 mL
2-10 oz	cans whole mushrooms, drained	2-284 mL
1 tbsp	soy sauce	15 mL
1/2 cup	onion, minced	125 mL
1 cup	celery, chopped	250 mL
1-3 oz	can chow mein noodles (optional)	85 g

In a mixing bowl, combine all ingredients except noodles. Place in a lightly buttered 2 qt (2 L) casserole dish. Cover and cook 30 minutes at 350 F (180 C). Add noodles the last 10 minutes of cooking. 6-8 servings.

Many of today's Christmas customs originated with the pagan celebrations of the Winter Solstice. The return of light as the days became longer, were signified with great bonfires, burning of the Yule log, and the lighting of candles.

TURKEY SOUFFLE

1/4 cup	butter	50 mL
5 tbsp	flour	75 mL
1 1/4 cups	milk	300 mL
1/2 tsp	onion, minced	2 mL
2/3 tsp	salt	4 mL
	pepper to taste	
4	egg yolks, beaten	
4	egg whites, beaten	
1 1/2 cups	cooked turkey, diced	375 mL
1/2 cup	celery, diced	125 mL
4	egg whites, beaten	

In a saucepan, combine butter, flour, and milk to make a white sauce. Add onion and seasonings. In a bowl, add a small amount of white sauce to beaten egg yolks. Add turkey and celery to white sauce. Combine with egg yolks and mix thoroughly. Fold in stiffly beaten egg whites and pour mixture into a greased casserole dish. Oven poach 40 minutes at 375 F (190 C). 4-6 servings.

HAM TETRAZZINI

4 oz	pasta noodles	115 g
1/4 lb	mushrooms, sliced	125 g
1	small onion, finely chopped	
4 tbsp	butter	60 mL
3 tbsp	flour	45 mL
1 1/3 cups	chicken broth	325 mL
1/2 cup	milk (cream)	125 mL
pinch	salt, pepper, cayenne pepper, nutmeg, grated	
	Tobasco to taste	
2 cups	cooked ham, diced	500 mL
1/2 cup	almonds, blanched, slivered	125 mL
	sharp Cheddar cheese, grated	

Cook noodles according to instructions on package and set aside. In a skillet, sauté mushrooms and onion in 2 tbsp (30 mL) butter. In a saucepan, melt 2 tbsp (30 mL) butter and blend in flour. Add chicken broth and milk and cook until thickened. Add seasonings, ham, and almonds. Combine ham mixture with mushrooms and noodles. Place in a greased 2 qt (2 L) casserole dish. Top with cheese and cook 30 minutes at 350 F (180 C). 4-6 servings.

Holly brought into the house before Christmas Eve is deemed unlucky.

NICOISE SALAD DRESSING

2 tbsp	wine vinegar or ReaLemon lemon juice from concentrate	30 mL
1/4 tsp	salt	1 mL
pinch	black pepper	
1/4 tsp	dry mustard	1 mL
8 tbsp	olive oil	120 mL

In a blender or food processor, combine all ingredients. Makes 1/2 cup (125 mL).

POTATO SALAD

4	large boiled potatoes, diced	
1/4 cup	wine vinegar	50 mL
2 tsp	salt	10 mL
1/2 tsp	dry mustard	2 mL
1/4 cup	olive oil	50 mL
2 tbsp	green onions, finely chopped	30 mL

In a mixing bowl, combine vinegar, salt, and dry mustard together. Add potatoes and let stand 5 minutes. Add olive oil and green onions. Set aside for main salad.

SALAD

1	head of lettuce, Boston or Romaine	
2 cups	potato salad	500 mL
4	large tomatoes, cut in wedges	
3	hard-boiled eggs, quartered	
1-7 oz	can tuna, flaked	198 g
1/2 cup	black olives, drained	125 mL
2 cups	green beans, blanched and chilled	500 mL
1/2 cup	dressing	125 mL
3 tbsp	parsley, finely chopped	45 mL
1	red onion, thinly sliced	
1	green pepper, sliced in rounds	

Line a large, deep salad bowl with lettuce. In the bottom centre, place the potato salad. Arrange each ingredient in its own section. Spoon dressing over top. Toss only when ready to serve.

ALICE'S CAESAR SALAD

1	egg, whole	
1/2 cup	olive oil	125 mL
3 tbsp	ReaLemon lemon juice from concentrate	45 mL
1 tsp	salt	5 mL
3	green onions, chopped	
1/2 tsp	dry mustard	2 mL
4	garlic cloves, through press	
3	drops Worcestershire sauce	
4	anchovies, chopped	
	Romaine lettuce	
1/2 tsp	Parmesan cheese, grated	2 mL
	croutons	

In a blender or food processor, beat egg slowly. Add remaining ingredients, except for Parmesan cheese, one ingredient at a time and continue to beat slowly. Add Parmesan cheese and mix by hand. Pour dressing over Romaine lettuce and toss. Add Parmesan cheese and croutons.

AUNT MARY'S LEMON SALAD

1-6 oz	lemon jello	170 g
1/2	package unflavoured gelatin	5 g
1 cup	boiling water	250 mL
1 pt	lemon sherbet	1/2 L
1 1/2 cups	creamed cottage cheese	375 mL
1 cup	crushed pineapple, drained	250 mL

In a mixing bowl, combine lemon jello, gelatin, and boiling water. Stir until jello is dissolved. Add sherbet, cottage cheese and pineapple and mix until blended. Place in a serving dish and refrigerate until firm.

Christmas day, 1642, Sir Isaac Newton was born.

LIME JELLO MOULD

1-19 oz	can crushed pineapple, drained	540 mL
	water	
1-3 oz	lime jello	85 g
1 cup	cottage cheese	250 mL
1/2 cup	miracle whip	125 mL
1 tsp	horseradish	5 mL
1/4 cup	walnuts, finely chopped	50 mL

Drain pineapple and place juice in a measuring cup. Add enough water to make 1 cup (250 mL). In a saucepan, heat juice and water. Add jello and continue heating until dissolved. Cool. In a separate bowl, combine remaining ingredients. When jello is cool, add pineapple mixture to jello. Place in a serving dish and refrigerate until firm.

SALAD TO SERVE WITH COLD CUTS

1	package unflavoured gelatine	
1-10 oz	can tomato soup	284 mL
2-4 oz	packages cream cheese	2-125 g
1 cup	mayonnaise	250 mL
1/2 cup	celery, chopped	125 mL
1/4 cup	green pepper, chopped	50 mL
1/4 cup	onion, finely chopped	50 mL

In a saucepan, heat gelatine, soup, and cream cheese. Beat until smooth. Add remaining ingredients. Pour into a mould and refrigerate until firm.

"I'll be spending a typical American Christmas. My tree is from Canada, the ornaments from Hong Kong. The lights come from Japan—and the idea from Bethlehem!"
  Robert Orben

FRUIT AND CHICKEN SALAD

1 1/2 cups	cooked chicken, diced	375 mL
1/2 cup	celery, diced	125 mL
1/2 cup	Mandarin oranges (crushed pineapple), drained	125 mL
1/2 cup	seedless grapes	125 mL
1 tbsp	salad oil	15 mL
1 tbsp	pineapple juice	15 mL
1 tbsp	vinegar	15 mL
1/4 cup	almonds, blanched, slivered, toasted	50 mL
1/4 cup	mayonnaise	50 mL

In a large mixing bowl, combine chicken, celery and fruits. In a separate bowl, prepare dressing of salad oil, juice, and vinegar. Pour over chicken mixture and let stand 1 hour. Place salad in a serving bowl, leaving behind excess liquid. Add almonds and combine with mayonnaise. Serve on lettuce. 4-6 servings.

CURRIED CHICKEN SALAD

1 cup	cooked chicken, diced	250 mL
1/2 cup	apple, diced	125 mL
1/2 cup	seedless raisins	125 mL
1 cup	celery, diced	250 mL
1/4 cup	green pepper, chopped	50 mL
1/4 cup	green onion, finely chopped	50 mL
1/2 cup	mayonnaise	125 mL
1/2 tsp	curry powder	2 mL
1/8 tsp	salt	0.5 mL
1/8 tsp	pepper	0.5 mL
	lemon, sliced	

In a large mixing bowl, combine chicken, fruits, and vegetables. Add mayonnaise and seasonings and combine well. Serve on lettuce or avocado halves. Garnish with lemon.

The first Canadian Christmas carol was written in the Huron tongue in 1641, by the Jesuit missionary.

On facing page: **Fruit and Chicken Salad**, page 88.

Santa's Bakeshop

RAISIN BUNS

1/2 cup	white raisins	125 mL
1/2 cup	dark raisins	125 mL
1/4 cup	Brandy (water)	50 mL
3 1/2 cups	flour, sifted	875 mL
1	package active dry yeast	
2 tbsps	sugar	30 mL
1/3 cup	water, lukewarm	75 mL
4	eggs, slightly beaten	
1 cup	butter, softened	250 mL
1/4 tsp	cinnamon	1 mL
1/2 tsp	lemon peel, grated	2 mL
1	egg yolk	
3 tbsps	milk	45 mL

Soak raisins overnight in Brandy. In a mixing bowl, combine 1/2 cup (125 mL) flour, yeast, sugar, and water. Moisten hands and form dough into a ball. Immerse ball of dough in warm water. Let rise to the surface (about 15 minutes). In a large mixing bowl, combine 2 cups (500 mL) flour, salt, eggs, 1/4 cup (50 mL) butter, cinnamon and peel. Mix to form a soft dough. Remove dough ball from water. Shake off excess water and combine with other dough, (will be soft and sticky). Throw dough onto unfloured pastry board. Remove with spatula and continue to throw dough onto pastry board from a height of 20'' (50 cm), until dough is smooth and no longer sticks to the board, (about 10 minutes). Blend in remaining butter. DO NOT KNEAD. Add raisins. Place dough in a buttered bowl. Cover with a damp cloth and let rise until double in size (2-3 hours). Punch dough down. Let rise again until double in size (2 hours). Punch down again. Fill buttered, floured muffin tins 2/3 full. Let rise until doubled. Combine egg yolk and milk and brush top of rolls. Bake 10 minutes at 425 F (220 C). Remove from pan immediately and serve warm. Makes 18-2 1/2'' (6 cm) rolls.

. . .one of Riel's men brought before us a steaming boiler of hot coffee and sugar and milk, along with a clothesbasket brimming with delicious buttered buns.''
R.P. Ottewell.

CHRISTMAS BREAD

2	packages active dry yeast	
1/4 cup	warm water	50 mL
1 cup	milk	250 mL
1/3 cup	butter	75 mL
1/4 cup	sugar	50 mL
1/2 tsp	salt	2 mL
1	egg	
3 1/2 cups	flour, all-purpose	875 mL

filling

1/4 cup	sugar	50 mL
2 tbsps	butter	30 mL
1/2 tsp	cinnamon	2 mL
1 cup	raisins	250 mL
1/2 cup	candied orange peel, chopped	125 mL
1/2 cup	citron, chopped	125 mL
1/4 cup	almonds, blanched, slivered	50 mL

topping

1	egg	
1 tsp	water	5 mL
1/2 cup	almonds, blanched,slivered	125 mL

Dissolve yeast in warm water. In a saucepan, heat milk and add to butter, sugar, and salt. Let stand 10 minutes. Add yeast and remaining ingredients. Blend until smooth with a wooden spoon. Turn out on a floured pastry board and roll and knead 5 minutes. Place in a lightly greased bowl, cover and set in a warm place. Let rise 40-50 minutes until double in bulk. Knead again 10 times. Roll into a large rectangle. In a mixing bowl, thoroughly combine all ingredients for filling. Spread evenly over dough, leaving 1" (2.5 cm) at all sides. Roll up lengthwise and place seam-side down on a greased cookie sheet. Shape like a horseshoe and cover. Set in a warm place, about an hour, until double in size. Brush surface with beaten egg and water. Sprinkle with almonds. Bake 20-25 minutes at 375 F (190 C). Bread is done when it sounds hollow when rapped with a spoon. Cool on wire rack keeping bread covered with a towel. Serve warm.

"For Christmas dinner there was the tender, juicy roasted turkey. There were the sweet potatoes baked in the ashes and carefully wiped so that you could eat the good skins too. There was a loaf of salt rising bread made from the last of the white flour.
Laura Ingles Wilder, **Christmas On The Prairie**

PUMPKIN BREAD

2 2/3 cups	sugar	650 mL
2/3 cup	vegetable oil	150 mL
1 tsp	cloves	5 mL
1/2 tsp	nutmeg	2 mL
2 cups	pumpkin	500 mL
1 tsp	soda	5 mL
1/2 tsp	baking powder	2 mL
4	eggs	
1 1/2 tsps	salt	7 mL
1 tsp	cinnamon	5 mL
2/3 cup	hot water	150 mL
3 1/3 cups	flour	825 mL
1 cup	walnuts, finely chopped (optional)	250 mL

In a large mixing bowl, combine all ingredients, except walnuts, and mix well. Add walnuts and stir by hand. Pour batter into a greased 9 x 5 x 3″ (2 L) loaf pan, or muffin tins. Bake 15-20 minutes at 400 F (200 C). Remove from pan and cool.

CRANBERRY NUT BREAD

2 1/2 cups	biscuit mix	625 mL
1/2 cup	sugar	125 mL
1/4 cup	flour	50 mL
1	egg	
1 cup	milk	250 mL
2 tbsps	orange peel, grated	30 mL
3/4 cup	cranberries, chopped	175 mL
1/2 cup	nuts, chopped	125 mL

In a mixing bowl, combine biscuit mix, sugar, flour, egg, milk, and peel. Beat vigorously. Stir in cranberries and nuts by hand. Pour batter into a greased 9 x 5 x 3″ (2 L) loaf pan, or muffin tins. Bake 50-60 minutes at 350 F (180 C). Remove from pan and cool.

In England, it was believed that bread baked on Christmas day would never become mouldy.

CAROLERS' CHOCOLATE LOAF

1/2 cup	butter	125 mL
3/4 cup	sugar	175 mL
2	eggs	
2-1 oz	squares unsweetened chocolate , melted	2-28g
1 tsp	vanilla	5 mL
1 1/4 cups	pastry flour, sifted	300 mL
2 tsps	baking powder	10 mL
1/4 tsp	salt	1 mL
3/4 cup	milk	175 mL
1/2 cup	walnuts, chopped	125 mL
1 cup	rolled oats, uncooked	250 mL
	frosting (optional)	

In a mixing bowl or food processor, beat butter until creamy. Add sugar and continue to beat until fluffy. Add eggs, chocolate and vanilla and mix well. In a separate bowl, sift flour, baking powder and salt. Add to creamed mixture alternately with milk. Stir in nuts and oats by hand. Pour batter into a greased and floured loaf pan and bake for 50 minutes at 350 F (180 C). Cool and frost or serve plain.

DATE LOAF

1 cup	dates, chopped	250 mL
1/2 tsp	baking soda	2 mL
3/4 cup	hot water (coffee)	175 mL
2/3 cup	brown sugar	150 mL
2 tbsps	butter	30 mL
1	egg, beaten	
1 1/2 cups	flour	375 mL
1 tsp	baking powder	5 mL
1/2 tsp	salt	2 mL
3/4 cup	walnuts, chopped (optional)	175 mL

In a measuring cup, place dates and soda and add hot water. Cool until lukewarm. In a mixing bowl, combine dates, sugar, butter and beaten egg. Sift in dry ingredients and stir in nuts. Pour batter into 1 large or 2 small loaf pans. Bake 45 minutes (large) or 35 minutes (small) at 325 F (160 C).

"Carol" means a song in which a religious topic is treated in a familiar or festive style. It was under the influence of Francis of Assisi, in the 13th century, that the carol became popular.

SALLY'S DATE MUFFINS

1/4 cup	shortening	50 mL
1/2 cup	brown sugar	125 mL
1	egg	
1 1/2 cups	flour, all purpose	375 mL
2 tsps	baking powder	10 mL
1 cup	dates, chopped	250 mL
1 tsp	baking soda	5 mL
	boiling water	

In a mixing bowl, cream shortening and add sugar and egg. Beat well. Sift in flour, and baking powder. Place dates in a 1 cup measuring cup. Add baking soda and fill cup to the 1 cup (250 mL) line with boiling water. Combine all ingredients stirring only until blended. Fill cupcake papers 3/4 full and bake 10-15 minutes at 400 F (200 C).

MINCEMEAT MUFFINS

1	egg, beaten	
1/2 cup	mincemeat	125 mL
1/2 cup	apple juice	125 mL
1-14 oz	package oatmeal muffin mix	900 g
1 tsp	orange peel, grated	5 mL
1 cup	icing sugar	250 mL
4 tsps	milk	20 mL
1/2 tsp	rum extract	2 mL

In a mixing bowl, thoroughly combine beaten egg, mincemeat, and apple juice. Stir in muffin mix and orange peel. Pour batter into greased muffin tins until half full. Bake 15 minutes, until golden brown, at 400 F (200 C). Remove from tins immediately. In a small bowl, combine icing sugar, milk and rum extract. Pour over warm muffins and serve.

For good luck, mincemeat of tartlet size is to be eaten every day between Christmas Day and Twelfth Night.

CHRISTMAS COFFEE CAKE

2 cups	biscuit mix	500 mL
3/4 cup	milk	175 mL
1/3 cup	butter, melted	75 mL
3 tbsps	brown sugar	45 mL
12	Maraschino cherries	
1/3 cup	hazelnuts	75 mL
	cinnamon	
	sugar	

In a large mixing bowl, blend biscuit mix and milk and shape dough into 12 balls. Pour half the melted butter into a 9″ (1 L) ring pan and sprinkle with brown sugar, cherries, and nuts. Roll 12 dough balls in other half of butter and place in ring pan. Sprinkle balls with cinnamon and sugar to taste. Bake 25-30 minutes at 400 F (200 C). Remove from pan while warm.

JILL'S CRANBERRY LOAF CAKE

2 cups	flour	500 mL
1 cup	sugar	250 mL
1 1/2 tsps	baking powder	7 mL
1/2 tsp	soda	2 mL
1 tsp	salt	5 mL
1/4 cup	shortening	50 mL
1	egg, well beaten	
3/4 cup	orange juice	175 mL
1 cup	cranberry sauce	250 mL
	OR	
1-2 cups	fresh cranberries	250-500 mL
1/2 cup	nuts, chopped (optional)	125 mL

Sift dry ingredients together. Cut in shortening until mixture is crumbly. In a separate bowl, mix egg and orange juice. Pour orange juice mixture, all at once, into dry ingredients. Mix just enough to dampen. Add cranberries and nuts. Spoon batter into greased loaf pan. Bake at 350 (180 C) for 1 hour. Remove from pan and cool on rack.

Christmas caroling passed from Italy to France and Germany and later to England.

CRANBERRY COFFEE CAKE

2 tbsps	cranberry sauce	30 mL
1 1/2 cups	milk	375 mL
2 cups	flour	500 mL
1 tsp	soda	5 mL
2 cups	sugar	500 mL
1 tsp	cinnamon	5 mL
1 tsp	cloves	5 mL

In a mixing bowl, combine cranberry sauce and milk. Sift in flour and soda; add remaining ingredients. Pour batter into lightly greased and floured 9″ (2 L) square baking pan. Bake 3 minutes at 375 F (190 C). Serve warm or store. Cake improves with age. May also be frozen and re-heated.

SPICE CAKE

1 cup	sugar	250 mL
1/2 cup	butter	125 mL
1/2 cup	shortening	125 mL
1/4 tsp	nutmeg, grated	1 mL
1/2	lemon, juice and rind	
1 cup	currants	250 mL
1 cup	raisins	250 mL
1/4 cup	mixed candied peel, finely chopped	50 mL
3 1/2 cups	flour	875 mL
3	egg yolks, beaten	
2 tsps	baking powder	10 mL
1/2 cup	milk	125 mL
3	egg whites, beaten	
1	egg white	
	almonds, blanched	
	candied fruit	
	frosting (optional)	

In a large mixing bowl, cream sugar, butter, shortening and nutmeg. Dredge fruit with a sprinkling of flour and set aside. Add beaten egg yolks to sugar mixture. Sift in flour and powder and alternately add milk. Fold in fruits and beat vigorously. Fold in 3 beaten egg whites. Pour batter into greased 9 x 5 x 3″ (2 L) loaf pan, lined with wax paper. Glaze top with egg white and bake for 1 1/2 hours at 300 F (150 C). Decorate cake with blanched almonds or candied fruits, or glaze with frosting.

Spice cake orignated in Christmas celebrations in Germany.

MEG'S RUM CAKE

1 cup	walnuts, chopped (pecans)	250 mL
1-18.5 oz	package yellow cake mix	570 g
1-3.75 oz	package instant vanilla pudding mix	85 g
4	eggs	
1/2 cup	cold water	125 mL
1/2 cup	vegetable oil	125 mL
1/2 cup	dark Rum	125 mL
glaze		
1/4 lb	butter	125 g
1/4 cup	water	125 mL
1 cup	white sugar	250 mL
1/2 cup	Rum	125 mL

Grease and flour a 10″ (25 cm) tube pan or a 12-cup (4 L) Bundt pan. Sprinkle nuts over bottom of pan. In a mixing bowl, combine cake mix, pudding mix, eggs, water, oil and Rum. Pour batter over nuts. Bake 1 hour at 325 F (160 C). Cool. To make glaze, melt butter in a saucepan. Stir in water and sugar. Boil 5 minutes stirring constantly. Remove from heat and stir in rum. Using a skewer, pierce cake all over while still in pan. Pour most of glaze over cake and let sit until absorbed. Invert cake on a serving plate and pour remaining glaze on top.

WHOLE WHEAT GINGERBREAD

1/2 cup	butter or margarine	125 mL
2 tbsp	sugar	30 mL
3/4 cup	light molasses	175 mL
2 cups	whole wheat flour	500 mL
1/2 tsp	salt	2 mL
3/4 tsp	baking soda	3 mL
1 tsp	ginger	5 mL
1/2 tsp	cinnamon	2 mL
1/2 tsp	nutmeg, grated	2 mL
1/2 cup	walnuts, chopped	125 mL
1/2 cup	raisins	125 mL
2	eggs	
1/2 cup	milk	125 mL

In a saucepan, melt butter. Add sugar and molasses and stir. In a mixing bowl, sift together flour, salt, soda and spices. Stir in nuts and raisins. In a separate bowl, beat eggs and milk and combine with molasses mixture. Mix together wet and dry ingredients with a wooden spoon, until blended. Pour batter into a greased 8 x 8 x 2″ (2 L) pan. Bake 40 minutes at 350 F (180 C).

OLD-FASHIONED GINGERBREAD

1 2/3 cups	flour	400 mL
1 tsp	baking soda	5 mL
1/4 tsp	salt	1 mL
2 tsps	cinnamon	10 mL
1/2 tsp	cloves	2 mL
1 tsp	ginger	5 mL
1 cup	brown sugar	250 mL
1/2 cup	butter	125 mL
2	eggs	
3/4 cup	sour cream	175 mL
1/3 cup	raisins (optional)	75 mL
	flour	
	whipped cream (hard sauce)	

Sift flour, baking soda, salt, and spices and set aside. In a mixing bowl, cream sugar, and butter and add eggs, 1 at a time. Re-sift flour and add it alternately, with sour cream, to the sugar mixture. Fold in raisins. Pour batter into a buttered and lightly floured 9″ (2.5 L) square pan and bake 45-60 minutes at 325 F (160 C). Cool and serve with whipped cream.

LAYER CAKE GINGERBREAD

1 cup	honey	250 mL
1 tsp	ginger	5 mL
1 tsp	cinnamon	5 mL
1/2 tsp	cloves	2 mL
2 1/2 cups	flour, sifted	625 mL
1 tsp	baking powder	5 mL
1/2 tsp	salt	2 mL
1/2 cup	butter	125 mL
1 tsp	baking soda	5 mL
1/2 cup	brown sugar	125 mL
1	lemon, rind only, grated	
1	egg	
1 cup	buttermilk	250 mL
	whipped cream	
	orange rind, grated	
	semi-sweet chocolate, grated	

In a saucepan, bring honey and spices to a boil and cool. In a mixing bowl, sift flour, baking powder, and salt, and set aside. In another bowl, cream butter, baking soda and sugar. Add lemon rind and egg. Stir in flour mixture and buttermilk alternately. Pour batter into 2 buttered and floured 8″ (2 L) square pans and bake 35 minutes at 350 F (180 C). Cool and remove from pans. Spread a layer of whipped cream between the two cakes and on top. Garnish with orange rind and chocolate.

SNOWDRIFT CAKE

1/2 lb	butter	125 g
1-8oz	package cream cheese	250 g
1 1/2 cups	sugar	375 mL
1 1/2 tsps	vanilla	7 mL
4	eggs	
2 1/4 cups	cake flour, sifted	550 mL
2 tsps	baking powder	10 mL
1 lb	mixed candied fruit	500 g
1/4 cup	cake flour, sifted	50 mL
1/2 cup	pecans, coarsely chopped	125 mL
1/2 cup	pecans, finely chopped	125 mL
	icing sugar	

In a mixing bowl, blend butter, cheese, sugar and vanilla. Add eggs one at a time beating well. Sift in 2 1/4 cups (550 mL) flour and baking powder and mix well. In a separate bowl, combine 1/4 cup (50 mL) flour, fruit and coarsely chopped pecans. Fold into batter. Grease a 10″ (2 L) Bundt or angel cake pan and sprinkle with finely chopped pecans. Spoon in batter. Bake 70-80 minutes at 325 F (160 C). Cool in pan 5 minutes and remove. Continue to cool on a rack. Sprinkle with sifted icing sugar.

"Mary and Laura pulled out two small packages. They unwrapped them and each found a little heart-shaped cake. Over their delicate brown tops was sprinkled white sugar . . .It had been made of pure white flour and sweetened with sugar."
Laura Ingles Wilder, **Christmas On The Prairie**

YULE LOG CAKE

5	eggs, separated	
1/2 tsp	cream of tartar	2 mL
1 cup	icing sugar	250 mL
3 tbsps	flour	45 mL
1/4 tsp	salt	1 mL
pinch	pepper	
1 1/2 tsps	ginger	7 mL
1 tsp	allspice	5 mL
1 tsp	cinnamon	5 mL
1 tsp	nutmeg	5 mL
1 tsp	cardamon	5 mL
1/2 tsp	cloves	2 mL
1 1/2 tsps	instant coffee	7 mL
1 1/2 cups	whipping cream	375 mL
1/2 cup	sifted icing sugar	125 mL
1 1/2 tsps	vanilla	7 mL

In a mixing bowl, beat egg whites at room temperature with cream of tartar until soft peaks form. Gradually add 1/2 cup (125 mL) sifted confectioners' sugar. Beat until stiff peaks form. In a separate bowl, beat egg yolks until thick and light in colour. In another bowl, sift together 3 times, the remaining 1/2 cup (250 mL) icing sugar, flour, salt, pepper and spices. Add the instant coffee. Fold into egg yolk mixture until just blended. Gently fold yolk mixture into egg whites. Spread batter evenly in a jelly roll pan which has been greased, lined with wax paper, and greased again. Bake 15 minutes at 350 F (180 C). Cake will be springy to touch. Turn cake out on a towel sprinkled with sifted icing sugar. Peel off paper carefully. Starting at narrow end, roll cake and towel together; cool thoroughly on rack. Whip cream, gradually adding 1/2 cup (125 mL) icing sugar and vanilla. Unroll cake and spread with cream. Roll up again. Roll onto serving dish. Chill at least 3 hours. Sprinkle lightly with icing sugar.

Today's yule log is symbolic of what was at one time a firmly entrenched custom. A root or stump was brought home Christmas Eve. It was not purchased, but obtained from one's own land, or a neighbour's. The 'yule log' was placed in the fireplace or the kitchen hearth and lighted with a faggot saved from the previous year. The log was kept burning for twelve hours to ward off ill-luck. If it did not ignite the first time, it was a sign of bad luck.

TWELFTH NIGHT CAKE

1 cup	butter	250 mL
3/4 cup	brown sugar	175 mL
3	eggs	
1/4 cup	skim milk	50 mL
3 cups	flour	750 mL
3/4 cup	raisins	175 mL
3/4 cup	mixed candied fruit	175 mL
1/2 tsp	salt	2 mL
1/4 tsp	cinnamon	1 mL
1/4 tsp	nutmeg, grated	1 mL
1/4 tsp	allspice	1 mL
1/4 cup	almonds, blanched, finely chopped	50 mL

In a mixing bowl, cream butter and sugar until fluffy. Add eggs one at a time and beat each well. Blend in milk. Dredge fruit with a sprinkling of flour and sift remaining flour and dry ingredients into batter. Fold in fruit and almonds and beat vigorously. Grease a 9″ (2 L) tube pan and line with heavy waxed paper. Lightly grease the waxed paper and pour in batter. Bake for 2 1/2 hours at 250 F (120 C).

Twelfth Night Cake originated in Christmas celebrations in France. The cake was baked containing a bean and a pea. The man to find the bean in his slice, and the woman to find the pea, became the Twelfth Night King and Queen of the evening. The bean King derives from the Saturnalian King chosen by lot. In parts of France, Spain, and even Mexico, the tradition of baking the cake with the bean and pea still continues, although not in England. However, at Drury Lane Theatre, in London, a Twelfth Night Cake is still delivered to the actresses and actors in the Green Room, a practice first begun in 1794 by an actor who was also a chef.

CHRISTMAS FRUIT CAKE

FOR BEST RESULTS

MAKE fruit cake 2-6 weeks or more before serving.

INGREDIENTS, even spices, should be fresh.

CUT fruit with scissors and dip scissors in water to prevent fruit from sticking.

BLEND ingredients thoroughly at every stage of mixing. Use hands or a wooden spoon.

GREASE pan thoroughly with lard or butter, NEVER MARGARINE.

LINE bottom and sides of pan with 2 thicknesses of paper. Grease paper. Place 1 thickness of paper around outside of pan and tie with a string. These precautions ensure even cooking.

FILL pans to within 1″ (3 cm) of the top. Allow batter to settle, even stand overnight, before cooking.

COVER cake with brown paper or a tin pie plate for the first half of baking to prevent cake from becoming too crusty and dry. NEVER open the oven door during the first half of baking. Then do so carefully, closing the door gently.

SPACE cakes evenly on oven rack so heat can circulate freely.

BAKE, always in a slow oven, temperature between 250 F (120 C) and 325 F (160 C). A pan of warm water placed on the bottom rack of the oven and removed the last hour of baking prevents cake from cracking.

CAKE is done when the top feels firm to the touch. A broom straw or knitting needle inserted into the centre of the cake should come out clean. Cake should not be hissing when removed from the oven. If so, it requires more baking.

COOL cake slowly, in the pan, away from draught. Remove cake from pan; remove paper and cool further on a rack or tea towel. Cake must be cold before storing.

WRAP cake in cheesecloth or linen, soaked in Brandy or Wine, and then wrap in foil; or cake may be wrapped in several layers of brown paper and then foil. For long term storage, bury unwrapped cake in powdered sugar. Store all cake in a sealed container or heavy foil and keep in a cool place. Cakes have been kept up to twenty-five years!

DECORATE cake with nut meats or candied fruit. Hold in place by dipping the undersides in a glaze. Entire cake may be glazed or iced. Often, cake is not decorated or glazed until approximately 1 week before serving.

SERVE cake freshened with a sprinkling of Brandy, Wine, or Sherry, whatever has been used in baking the cake.

BURNT cake may be saved by removing charred pieces and icing, glazing or decorating. This remedies cracked and uneven cake as well.

DRY cake may be saved by pouring Brandy, Wine, or Sherry, used in baking the cake, through holes made with a skewer.

PAN FACTS

ODDLY shaped tins, measure contents with water and prepare 2/3 of that measurement in batter.

TIN cans make interesting give-away shapes. See index for standard can sizes.

A ROUND pan, of the same size as a square pan, is roughly 3/4 the area of the square pan.

Christmas cake is fun to bake and give as a gift. Baking in a variety of shapes and sizes may require the approximation of batter quantities and baking time which will vary slightly with every oven.

APPROXIMATED BAKING CHART FOR CHRISTMAS CAKE

pan	size in inches	batter amount in cups	oven temp.	baking time in hrs.
loaf	8 1/2 x 4 1/2 x 2 1/2	4-5	275 F	2
	21.25 x 11.25 x 6.25 cm	1-1.2 L	140 C	
loaf	5 1/2 x 3 x 2 1/2	1–2	275 F	1 1/2
	13.75 x 7.5 x 6.2 cm	250–500 mL	140 C	
loaf	4 1/2 x 3 x 2	1 1/2	275 F	1 1/4
	11.25 x 7.5 x 5 cm	375 mL	140 C	
loaf	4 1/2 x 2 1/2 x 1 1/2	1	275 F	1
	11.25 x 6.25 x 3.75 cm	250 mL	140 C	
round	4 1/2 x 1 1/2	1–1 1/4	300 F	1 1/3
	11.25 x 3.75 cm	250–300 mL	150 C	
tube	10 x 4	13	275 F	3 1/4
	25 x 10	3.25 L	140 C	
ring	7 1/2	3	275 F	1 2/3
	18.75 cm	750 mL	140 C	
1-lb	coffee tin	1 3/4	300 F	1
500 g		425 mL	150 C	
6-oz	juice can	1/2	300 F	1
170 g		125 mL	150 C	
2 1/2 oz	muffin tin	1/4	300 F	1
70 g		50 mL	150 C	

In Ireland, cakes baked on Christmas Eve and eaten during the holidays were thought to bring good luck and health. One cake was usually baked for each member of the family.

DARK CHRISTMAS CAKE I

2-2 oz	packages almonds, blanched, slivered	2-100 g
1 lb	candied cherries	500 g
2 cups	raisins	500 mL
1 cup	currants	250 mL
1 cup	dates, chopped	250 mL
1/2 cup	Brandy	125 mL
1/2 cup	flour	125 mL
2 cups	flour	500 mL
1/2 tsp	baking soda	2 mL
1 tsp	cloves	5 mL
1 tsp	allspice	5 mL
1 tsp	cinnamon	5 mL
1/2 tsp	salt	2 mL
1 cup	butter	250 mL
2 cups	brown sugar, lightly packed	500 mL
6	eggs	
3/4 cup	molasses	175 mL
3/4 cup	apple juice	175 mL

In a large bowl, combine fruit, nuts, and Brandy and let stand several hours or overnight. Dust fruit with 1/2 cup (125 mL) flour. In a separate bowl, sift 2 cups (500 mL) flour, soda, and spices and set aside. In a mixing bowl, cream remaining ingredients and gradually add to dry ingredients. Fold in fruit. Pour batter into prepared loaf pans. Bake for 3-3 1/2 hours at 275 F (140 C).

DARK CHRISTMAS CAKE II

1/2 cup	butter	125 mL
1 1/3 cups	brown sugar	325 mL
3	eggs, separated	
1 1/4 cups	flour, sifted	300 mL
1 tsp	baking powder	5 mL
1/4 tsp	salt	1 mL
1 tsp	cinnamon	5 mL
1/2 tsp	cloves	2 mL
1 1/2 tsp	ginger	7 mL
1 tsp	nutmeg	5 mL
2 cups	currants	500 mL
2 cups	seeded raisins	500 mL
1/4 cup	dark molasses	50 mL
1/4 cup	Sherry (juice)	50 mL
2 cups	candied citron, shredded	500 mL

On facing page: **Christmas Fruit Cake**, in a variety of shapes, pages 105-109, and *Applesauce Fruitcake Bars*, page 125.

DARK CHRISTMAS CAKE II cont.

In a mixing bowl, cream sugar and butter. Beat egg yolks until foamy and add to sugar mixture. Sift dry ingredients over currants and raisins and add to sugar mixture alternately with molasses and Sherry. Mix well, then fold in stiffly beaten egg whites. Pour batter into prepared pans and alternate each layer of batter with a layer of citron so there are three layers of citron and four layers of batter, ending with a batter layer. Bake 3-4 hours at 325 F (160 C).

DARK CHRISTMAS CAKE III

2 cups	seedless raisins	500 mL
2-8 oz	packages candied cherries, chopped	2-250 g
2 cups	candied pineapple, chopped	500 mL
3 cups	mixed peel, chopped	750 mL
2 1/4 cups	dates, chopped	550 mL
1/2 cup	Sherry	125 mL
4 cups	walnuts, chopped	1 L
5 cups	flour, all-purpose	1.25 L
1 tsp	nutmeg	5 mL
1 tsp	cloves	5 mL
1 tsp	ginger	5 mL
2 tsp	cinnamon	10 mL
1 tsp	baking soda	5 mL
1 1/2 tsp	salt	7 mL
1 lb	butter	500 g
2 1/2 cups	sugar	625 mL
7	eggs	
3/4 cup	molasses	175 mL

In a large bowl, combine fruit and soak in Sherry several hours or overnight. Add nuts and half the flour and set aside. In a bowl, sift remaining flour, spices, soda, and salt. In a mixing bowl, cream butter, sugar, and add eggs, 1 at a time mixing each thoroughly. Stir in molasses. Gradually stir in dry ingredients, then fold in fruit. Pour batter into prepared pans and bake 2-3 hours at 300 F (150 C).

Martha Washington's famous Christmas cake called for 40 eggs, the yolks and whites, to be separated.

AUNT EVA'S LIGHT CHRISTMAS CAKE

Aunt Eva first made this cake in 1927, and made it every Christmas.

1 cup	butter	250 mL
3/4 cup	sugar	175 mL
4	eggs, unbeaten	
1/2 tsp	almond extract	2 mL
2 tbsp	orange juice	30 mL
1	lemon, rind only, grated	
1 tsp	salt	5 mL
3 cups	flour	750 mL
1 cup	seedless raisins	250 mL
1 cup	almonds, blanched	250 mL
1 cup	seeded raisins	250 mL
1/4 cup	orange peel	150 mL
1/4 cup	lemon peel	50 mL
1 cup	candied pineapple, shredded	250 mL

In a mixing bowl, cream butter and add sugar, blending well. Add eggs, one at a time, unbeaten, and beat in thoroughly. Stir in extract, orange juice, and lemon rind. In a separate bowl, mix salt, flour, fruit and nuts. Add fruit mixture to batter. Pour batter into prepared pans and bake for 3 hours at 300 F (150 C). Makes 3 cakes.

WHITE FRUIT CAKE II

1/2 cup	butter	125 mL
1 cup	sugar	250 mL
2 cups	flour, sifted	500 mL
1/2 tsp	soda	2 mL
1 tsp	cream of tartar	5 mL
1/4 tsp	salt	1 mL
6	egg whites, beaten	
1 lb	citron, chopped	500 g
3/4 lb	almonds, blanched, sliced	375 g
1/2 cup	coconut, shredded	125 mL

WHITE FRUIT CAKE II cont.

In a mixing bowl, cream butter and sugar, then add sifted flour, soda, cream of tartar, and salt. Fold in stiffly beaten egg whites. Add 1/3 of the citron to the batter. Pour batter into prepared pans and alternate each layer of batter with a layer of citron, nuts, and coconut. Repeat alternate layers ending with a layer of batter. Bake 1 hour at 325 F (160 C). Makes 2 cakes.

WHITE FRUIT CAKE III

3/4 lb	butter	375 g
2 cups	sugar	500 mL
1/2 lb	seedless white raisins	250 g
3/4 lb	citron, chopped	375 g
3/4 lb	candied cherries, chopped	375 g
1 lb	almonds, blanched	500 g
1 oz	brandy	65 mL
5 oz	rose water	155 mL
10	eggs	
2 tbsp	almond extract	30 mL
4 cups	flour, sifted	1 L

In a mixing bowl, cream butter and sugar and set aside. In a large bowl, combine fruit and nuts and soak in brandy and rose water. Add eggs, one at a time, to butter mixture and beat each well. Add extract. Gradually stir in flour and fold in fruit mixture. Pour batter into prepared pans and bake 2 hours at 275 F (140 C).

WHITE FRUIT CAKE IV

2 cups	mixed candied fruit	500 mL
1 cup	mixed candied peel	250 mL
1 cup	red and green cherries	250 mL
8 oz	candied pineapple	250 g
1/2 cup	dried apricots	125 mL
1/2 cup	dried figs	125 mL

1 cup	sultana raisins	250 mL
2 cups	almonds, blanched, slivered	500 mL
2 cups	coconut, flaked	500 mL
2 cups	flour, sifted	500 mL
1 1/2 tsp	baking powder	7 mL
1 tsp	salt	5 mL
1 cup	butter, softened	250 mL
1 cup	sugar	250 mL
5	eggs	
2 tsp	vanilla	10 mL
1/2 cup	pineapple juice	125 mL

Chop fruit and combine with nuts in a large bowl. Sift in flour, baking powder, and salt. In a mixing bowl, cream butter and sugar. Add eggs, one at a time, and beat each well. Stir in vanilla and juice. Add fruit mixture and blend. Pour batter into prepared pans and pack down well. Bake 2 hours at 275 F (140 C). Makes 2 cakes.

"Here, too, were the dried fruits, the raisins, currants, cherries, citron and angelica for the Christmas cakes and puddings. Mamma had brought her supply of these on an earlier expedition, and our Christmas cakes had been made. Everyone in the house had stirred a wish into them before they were put in the oven to bake for hours. Then, for two or three days they had stood on trays in the pantry while juice from preserved cherries and plums was poured over them and allowed to soak in. Finally they had been bathed in brandy and now, blanketed under an inch of almond paste they were dozing boozily in the fruit cellar."
    Ruth Harvey, **For The Yuletide Feast**

WANDA'S BLACK FOREST CAKE

bottom layer

3/4 cup	All purpose flour	175 mL
1 tbsp	cocoa	15 mL
1 tsp	baking powder	5 mL
1/3 cup	sugar	75 mL
1 pkg	vanilla sugar	9 g
1	egg white	
1/2 cup	butter (margarine)	125 mL

In a mixing bowl, sift flour, cocoa, and baking powder. Add sugars and partially mix. Cut in butter. Knead into a smooth ball, then roll out onto the bottom of a greased spring form pan. Bake 20 min. at 350° F (180°C).

middle/top layer

4	egg yolks	
2 tbsp	warm water	30 mL
1 cup	sugar	250 mL
1 pkg	vanilla sugar	9 g
3 drops	bitter almond baking oil	
1/4 tsp	cinnamon	1 mL
4	egg whites	
3/4 cup	flour	175 mL
1-1/2 tsp	baking powder	7 mL
5 tbsp	cocoa	75 mL
3/4 cup	corn starch	175 mL

In a mixing bowl or food processor, beat egg yolks and water. While beating, add 2/3 of sugar and vanilla sugar. Beat until creamy; add spices. In a separate bowl beat egg whites until very stiff. Add remaining sugars. Place egg whites on top of creamy mixture. Sift remaining dry ingredients on top of egg whites. Carefully fold egg whites and flour under creamy mixture until combined. DO NOT STIR. Place in a lined spring form pan and bake 30-35 minutes at 350° F (180°C).

filling

1-14 oz can	sour cherries drained, reserve juice	75 oz.
4 tbsp	corn starch	60 mL
1 tbsp	powdered sugar	15 mL
1 pkg	vanilla sugar	9 g
2 pkgs	whipping cream stiffner	

Heat half the cherry juice until it boils and remove from heat. To other half of juice, stir in cornstarch. Add juices together, return to heat, and boil. Add cherries and sugars and refrigerate until cool. Whip cream and add stiffner only when ready to assemble cake.

It is generally believed the Christmas tree originated in Alsace and the Black Forest. St. Boniface, an English 8th century missionary to Germany, adorned a fir tree in tribute to the Christ child.

STEAMED PUDDINGS

FOR BEST RESULTS

MAKE pudding 1 month or even the summer before serving.

INGREDIENTS, especially suet, should be fresh.

CUT fruit with scissors and dip scissors in water to prevent fruit from sticking.

BLEND ingredients thoroughly at every stage of mixing. Traditionally, every member of the family stirs the pudding. The more stirring, the better. Use hands or a wooden spoon.

CONSISTENCY of pudding should be thin. Let stand, covered, in a cool place, overnight. Batter will stiffen from standing, but should still be soft.

GREASE mould with butter and sprinkle with sugar.

STIR batter and fill mould 3/4 full. Press batter down to prevent air holes.

SEAL mould with tight fitting lid, or cover with 2-3 thicknesses of greaseproof paper, greased on the underside with butter. Tie the mould under the rim with string and trim excess paper so it is clear of the water. Wrap mould in a sterile pudding cloth or heavy foil.

PLACE mould on a rack in a large kettle. Add boiling water to 1/2 way up side of mould. Place lid on kettle and keep on high heat until steam escapes from kettle. Reduce heat to a steady boil and continue to steam. Add more boiling water if necessary.

STEAM 6-8 hours, the longer the better. Long steaming darkens the pudding and enables it to store better.

COOL pudding in coverings, until they are dry. Remove pudding cloth or foil. If greaseproof paper is soggy, remove and replace. Re-foil and *STORE* pudding in a cool, dry place, *NEVER* in a tin.

STEAM 1-2 hours when ready to serve.

FLAME pudding to burn off any grease and add flavour by pouring 2 tbsp brandy over pudding and lighting.

SERVE with sauce.

" . . .the plum pudding as we know it today—firm and solid, sleekly rounded, dark and gleaming of complexion, and filled to bursting with every sort of fruit and sweetmeat except—and this is rather odd—plums."
Silas Spitzer, **Christmas Plum Pudding**

The earliest record of plum pudding is during the reign of Queen Anne. Plum pudding or "hackin" was traditionally made from 'hacked' fruit and vegetables, left to soak in liquor, and then decorated with holly.

SERVING QUANTITIES

2 pints (1 L)	6 people
1 1/2 pints (1.5 L)	4–6 people
1 pint (500 mL)	4 people

SUET PUDDING

2 cups	pastry flour	500mL
2 tsp	baking soda	10 mL
1/2 tsp	cinnamon	2 mL
2 cups	raisins	500 mL
1 lb	whole candied cherries	500 g
1 lb	mixed peel	500 g
1 1/2 cup	currants	375 mL
2 cups	bread crumbs, fine	500 mL
2 cups	suet, chopped	500 mL
2 cups	brown sugar, lightly packed	500 mL
2	eggs	
1/3 cup	molasses	75 mL
2 cups	buttermilk	500 mL
1/2 cup	almonds, blanched, slivered	125 mL

In a bowl, sift flour, soda, and cinnamon and set aside. In another bowl, combine fruit and sprinkle with 1/2 cup (125 mL) flour mixture and set aside. Add bread crumbs to remaining flour mixture. In a mixing bowl, combine suet, brown sugar, eggs, and molasses. Add dry ingredients, alternately, with buttermilk. Stir in fruit and almonds. Pour batter into prepared 2 qt (2 L) mould and steam 3-4 hours. 8 servings.

" . . . when dinner was ended the big plum pudding would be carried in studded with peeled almonds and sprigs of holly . . ."
James Joyce, A Portrait Of The Artist As A Young Man

CHRISTMAS PUDDING I

1/3 cup	butter	75 mL
3/4 cup	brown sugar	175 mL
1	egg, beaten	
2 tbsp	Wine	30 mL
1/2 cup	currants	125 mL
1/2 cup	raisins	125 mL
1/2 cup	dates, chopped	125 mL
1/3 cup	candied pineapple, chopped	75 mL
1/3 cup	candied cherries, chopped	75 mL
1/3 cup	pecans, chopped	75 mL
1/3 cup	citron, chopped	75 mL
1 cup	flour, sifted	250 mL
1/2 tsp	soda	2 mL
1/8 tsp	allspice	0.5 mL
1/8 tsp	ginger	0.5 mL
1/8 tsp	nutmeg, grated	0.5 mL
1/4 tsp	salt	1 mL
1/4 tsp	cinnamon	1 mL

In a mixing bowl, cream butter, sugar, and egg. Add Wine, fruits, and nuts. Sift in flour and spices and stir thoroughly. Spoon batter into a 1 qt (1 L) prepared mould and steam 4 hours. 4 servings.

CHRISTMAS PUDDING II

1/2 lb	suet	250 g
1/2 lb	brown sugar	250 g
1/4 lb	flour	125 g
1/4 lb	bread crumbs	125 g
1/2 lb	raisins	250 g
1/2 lb	sultanas	250 g
1/2 lb.	currants	250 g
1/4 lb	mixed peel	125 g
2 oz	almonds, chopped	70 g
1/2 tsp	nutmeg, grated	
1 tsp	cinnamon	5 mL
1/2 cup	milk	125 mL
4	eggs	
1 tbsp	marmalade	15 mL
4 oz	Brandy	125 mL
1	lemon, juice only	
1	carrot, grated	
1	small apple, grated	

CHRISTMAS PUDDING II cont.

In a mixing bowl, combine thoroughly, all dry ingredients. Add milk, egg, and marmalade. Stir in Brandy, lemon juice, carrot and apple and mix well. Spoon batter into prepared moulds and steam 6 hours.

In half a minute Mrs. Cratchit entered—flushed but smiling proudly—with the pudding, like a speckled cannonball, so hard and firm, blazing in half of a half a quartern of ignited brandy . . ."
Charles Dickens, A Christmas Carol

CHRISTMAS PUDDING III

1/2 cup	milk	125 mL
2 cups	bread crumbs, fine, white	500 mL
1 1/4 cups	brown sugar	300 mL
1/2 tsp	salt	2 mL
6	eggs, beaten	
1 cup	flour	250 mL
1 tsp	baking powder	5 mL
1/2 tsp	cinnamon	2 mL
1/2 tsp	cloves	2 mL
1/2 tsp	allspice	2 mL
2 1/2 cups	suet, finely chopped	625 mL
2 cups	currants	500 mL
4 cups	seeded raisins, halved	1 L
1/2 cup	figs, chopped	125 mL
1/2 cup	candied cherries, chopped	125 mL
1 cup	peel, shredded	250 mL
1/2 cup	almonds, blanched, shredded	125 mL
1	large carrot, grated	
1	lemon, juice and grated rind	
1/4 cup	Wine (grape juice)	50 mL

In a large bowl, soak bread crumbs in milk. Add sugar, salt, and beaten eggs. Sift in flour, baking powder, and spices. Add suet, fruits, nuts, and vegetables. Stir in wine and mix thoroughly. Spoon batter into prepared moulds and steam 6 hours. Makes about 4 lbs (2 kgs).

Christmas pudding was always stirred from East to West, in honor of the three Wise Men, and by every member of the family.

" . . . there was no lack of Christmas cheer in the shape of a large plum pudding to which our little ones did ample justice."
Catherine Parr Traill

THRIFTY PUDDING

1/3 cup	shortening (suet)	75 mL
1 cup	sugar	250 mL
1 cup	raisins	250 mL
1 cup	candied cherries	250 mL
1 cup	raw potatoes, grated	250 mL
1 cup	raw carrots, grated	250 mL
1 cup	flour, sifted	250 mL
1/2 tsp	salt	2 mL
1/2 tsp	cloves	2 mL
1 tsp	soda	5 mL
1 tsp	nutmeg, ground	2 mL
1 tsp	allspice	5 mL
2 tsp	cinnamon	10 mL

In a mixing bowl, cream shortening and sugar and add fruits, vegetables, and sifted dry ingredients. Spoon mixture into a prepared mould and steam 3 hours. 10 servings.

BREAD PUDDING

8 oz	stale white bread	20 g
	cold water	
2	eggs	
6 tbsp	butter, melted	90 mL
1/2 cup	sultanas	125 mL
1/4 cup	currants	50 mL
1/2 cup	raisins	125 mL
1/3 cup	mixed peel	75 mL
1 cup	brown sugar	250 mL
3/4 cup	milk	175 mL

In a bowl, soak bread in cold water for 2 hours and then squeeze out as much water as possible. In a mixing bowl, beat bread with fork and beat in eggs and melted butter. Add remaining ingredients and combine thoroughly. Pour batter into a lined, greased loaf pan. Bake for 1 1/2 hours at 325 F (160 C). Serve hot or cold in slices.

TRADITIONAL MINCEMEAT I

1/2 lb	ground beef	250 g
1 lb	suet, chopped	500 g
2 lb	brown sugar	1 kg
6-qt	basket spy apples, chopped	4 L
1 lb	raisins, seeded	500 g
1/2 lb	raisins, seedless	250 g
1 lb	currants	500 g
1/4 lb	candied peel	125 g
3/4 pt	sweet cider	375 mL
1/2 tbsp	molasses	7 mL
1/2 tbsp	vanilla	7 mL
1/2 tbsp	lemon extract	7 mL
1/2 tbsp	allspice	7 mL
1/2 tbsp	cinnamon	7 ml
1 tbsp	salt	15 mL
1/2 tbsp	nutmeg, grated	7 mL
2	lemons, juice only	
1 cup	fruit juice	250 mL

Stew beef and cool. In a mixing bowl combine all ingredients well. Let stand 2 weeks. Bottle in sterile jars. Can be frozen.

TRADITIONAL MINCEMEAT II

1 lb	ground beef	500 g
1/2 lb	suet, chopped	250 g
2 cups	currants	500 mL
2 cups	raisins	500 mL
6 cups	apples, grated	1.5 L
2 cups	brown sugar	500 mL
2/3 cup	molasses	150 mL
1 tsp	salt	5 mL
1 1/2 tsp	mace	7 mL
1 1/2 tsp	cinnamon	7 mL
1 1/2 tsp	cloves	7 mL
8 oz	orange peel	250 g
8 oz	citron peel	250 g
3/4 cup	cider vinegar	175 mL
1 cup	Brandy	250 mL

In a large pot, combine all ingredients except Brandy. Cover and simmer 2 hours. Stir frequently. Add Brandy and bottle in sterile jars. Age at least 1 month.

Mincemeat was originally made with mutton and ox-tongue. Mince pie was first called 'shrid pye', meaning shredded.

MEATLESS MINCEMEAT I

1 1/2 cups	apples, peeled and chopped	375 mL
1 cup	raisins, seeded	250 mL
1 cup	cranberries	250 mL
1/2 cup	cider vinegar	125 mL
3/4 cup	butter, melted	175 mL
pinch	salt	
2 tsp	cinnamon	10 mL
3/4 tsp	cloves	3 mL
3/4 tsp	allspice	3 mL
1 1/2 cups	sugar	375 mL
1 1/2 cups	grape juice	375 mL

In a large pot, combine all ingredients and cook 40 minutes, stirring occasionally. Bottle in sterile jars.

MEATLESS MINCEMEAT II

1	orange, seeds removed	
1	lemon, seeds removed	
1 1/2 cups	golden raisins	375 mL
1 1/2 cups	currants	375 mL
8	tart apples	
3/4 cup	mixed peed, diced	175 mL
1 3/4 cups	apple cider	425 mL
3 1/2 cups	brown sugar	875 mL
1 1/2 tsp	coriander	7 mL
1 1/2 tsp	cinnamon	7 mL
1 1/2 tsp	allspice	7 mL
1 1/2 tsp	mace	7 mL
1 1/2 tsp	nutmeg, grated	7 mL
1 1/2 tsp	cloves	7 mL
1/2 cup	brandy	125 mL
1/2 cup	rum	125 mL

Mince all fruit. In a large pot, combine fruit with cider and bring to a boil. Simmer, uncovered, for 15 minutes, until fairly dry. Add sugar, salt, and spices and simmer 15 minutes longer, until thick. Stir in brandy and rum. Use at once or bottle in sterile jars and store.

Mincemeat is a symbol of the gifts of the Wise Men, its composition being of the products of the East.

"Glorious time of great Too-much, . . .
Right thy most unthrifty glee,
And pious thy mince-piety."
  Leigh Hunt, **Christmas**

"A Christmas day, to be perfect, should be clear and cold,
with holly branches in berry, a blazing fire, a dinner with
mince pies, and games and forfeits in the evening."
  Leigh Hunt, *quoted in* **A Year Of Sunshine,** *selected by*
  Kate Sanborn

MEATLESS MINCEMEAT III

2	large lemons	
1 lb	tart apples, chopped	500 g
1/2 lb	suet, chopped	250 g
2 cups	currants	500 mL
1 cup	raisins, seeded	250 mL
1 cup	raisins, seedless	250 mL
1/2 cup	lemon peel	75 mL
2 tbsp	citron	30 mL
2 cups	sugar	500 mL
1 tbsp	allspice	15 mL
1 tbsp	cinnamon	15 mL
1 tbsp	nutmeg, grated	15 mL
1/4 cup	Brandy (Rum)	50 mL

Reserve the juice of the lemons. Boil lemon peels until tender and mash or place in a blender. In a mixing bowl, combine peels, suet and fruit. Add sugar and spices. Add lemon juice. Bottle in sterile jars, leaving space in each jar to add Brandy. Refrigerate. Stir occasionally. Use in 10 days.

"As many mince pies as you taste at Christmas, so many
happy months will you have."
  Old English Saying

"And then, at Christmas, tea, the recovered Uncles would be
jolly over their mince-pies . . ."
  Dylan Thomas, **Conversation About Christmas**

PIE FACTS

PASTRY	OVEN TEMPERATURE	BAKING TIME
pastry shell	450 F (233 C)	10–12 minutes
custard pie	400 F (205 C)	25–30 minutes
double crust pie		
cooked filling	400 F (205 C)	30–45 minutes
uncooked filling	400 F (205 C)	40–60 minutes
meringue	350 F (180 C)	12–15 minutes
frozen pie		
baked	325 F (160 C)	40–45 minutes
unbaked	425 F (218 C)	first 15 minutes
	375 F (190 C)	last 40–45 minutes

PASTRY

5 3/4 cups	flour	1.5 L
1 tbsp	salt	15 mL
1 lb	lard (NOT shortening)	500 g
2	eggs	
	water	

In a mixing bowl, combine flour and salt. Cut in lard. Place eggs in a measuring cup or blender and add enough water to make 1 cup. Mix thoroughly in blender and add to flour mixture. Combine well. Refrigerate until use

CRUMB CRUST

2 cups	graham cracker crumbs (chocolate wafer crumbs)	500 mL
1/4 cup	butter, melted	50 mL
1 tbsp	flour	30 mL
1/2 tsp	cinnamon (graham crust only)	2 mL

In a mixing bowl, combine all ingredients. Spread evenly in a pie plate and press firmly with the back side of a large spoon. Bake 10 minutes at 350 F (180 C).

RUM MINCE PIE

1 lb, 14 oz	mincemeat	900 g
1 1/2 cups	sliced peaches	375 mL
1-9″	pastry shell, unbaked	1 L
	pastry for lattice top	
3 tbsp	Rum	45 mL

In a bowl, combine mincemeat and peaches. Spoon mixture into unbaked pie shell. Top pie with a lattice or spoke crust and bake 30 minutes at 400 F (200 C), until browned. Remove pie from oven and spoon Rum through openings in crust. Serve warm. 6-8 servings.

RUM CUSTARD CHIFFON PIE

1	envelope gelatin	15 mL
1/4 cup	water, cold	50 mL
3	egg yolks	
3	egg whites	
1 1/2 cup	milk	375 mL
3/4 cup	sugar	175 mL
1/8 tsp	salt	0.5 mL
3 1/2 tbsp	Rum	52 mL
1-9″	pie shell, baked	1 L
	whipping cream, whipped	

Soften gelatine in water for 5 minutes. In a saucepan, beat egg yolks and add milk, 1/2 cup (125 mL) sugar, and salt. Cook over low heat continuously stirring until mixture coats spoon. Remove from heat and stir in gelatin. Cool until thick. Blend in Rum. Beat egg whites until stiff and add remaining sugar. Fold egg whites into custard. Pour mixture into baked pie shell. Garnish with whipped cream and serve.

" . . . my wife desirous to sleep, having sat up till four this morning seeing her maid make mince pies . . ."
Samuel Pepys, December 25th, 1666.

Before the reformation in England, mince pie was baked in an oblong pan and topped with a crust. When the crust sank in a concave manger form, a doll or Christ figure of dough was laid on top.

FROZEN GRASSHOPPER PIES

2-9″	chocolate wafer crumb crusts	2-1 L
1-14 oz	can Eagle Brand Sweetened Condensed Milk (NOT evaporated milk)	300 mL
1/3 cup	Crème de Menthe, green	75 mL
1/4 cup	Crème de Cacao	50 mL
2 cups	whipping cream, whipped chocolate curls (optional)	500 mL

In a large bowl, combine Sweetened Condensed Milk, Crème de Menthe and Crème de Cacao. Fold in whipped cream. Pour into crusts, cover and freeze 6 hours, or until firm. Garnish with chocolate curls. 16 servings.

GRASSHOPPER PIE

1-9″	chocolate wafer crumb crust	1 L
1	package large marshmallows	
1/4 cup	milk	50 mL
1/2 pt	whipping cream	250 mL
3 tbsp	Crème de Menthe, green	45 mL
2 tbsp	semi-sweet chocolate, grated	30 mL

In the top part of a double boiler, heat 25 marshmallows with milk and 1/4 cup (50 mL) of cream until marshmallows are partially melted. Remove from heat and stir until marshmallows are completely melted. Cool. Whip remaining cream and fold into mixture along with Crème de Menthe. Fill crumb crust and garnish top with chocolate. Refrigerate until serving. 6-8 servings.

BLACK BOTTOM PIES

3	eggs, separated	
1-14 oz	can Eagle Brand Sweetened Condensed Milk (NOT evaporated milk)	300 mL
2-1 oz	squares unsweetened chocolate	2-28 g
2-9″	chocolate wafer crumb crusts	2-L
1	envelope gelatine, unflavoured	
1/4 cup	water	50 mL
1-16 oz	container sour cream	500 mL
2 tbsp	light Rum	30 mL
1/4 cup	sugar	50 mL
	chocolate curls (opitonal)	

On facing page: **Grasshopper Pie**, page 124.

BLACK BOTTOM PIES cont.

In a small saucepan, beat egg yolks and add 2/3 cup Sweetened Condensed Milk and chocolate. Cook over low heat until chocolate melts and mixture thickens (about 3 minutes). Divide mixture in half and pour into crumb crusts. In a small saucepan, mix gelatine with water and let stand 1 minute. Stir over low heat until gelatine is dissolved. Remove from heat. In a large bowl, combine remaining Sweetened Condensed Milk, sour cream and rum. Stir in gelatine mixture. Chill until mixture mounds from a spoon. In a small mixing bowl, beat egg whites until soft peaks form and gradually add sugar. Beat until stiff. Fold into gelatine mixture. Pour over chocolate layer. Chill 4 hours or until set. Garnish with chocolate. 16 servings.

PUMPKIN PIE

2	eggs, slightly beaten	
3/4 cup	sugar	175 mL
1 1/2 tsp	cinnamon	7 ml
1/2 tsp	nutmeg, grated	2 mL
1/2 tsp	ginger	2 mL
1/4 tsp	allspice	1 mL
1/4 tsp	cloves	1 mL
1/2 tsp	salt	2 mL
1-16 oz	can pumpkin	398 mL
3 tbsp	molasses	45 mL
2-6 oz	cans evaporated milk	2-170 g
1-9″	pie shell, unbaked	1 L
1	egg white, unbeaten	
	whipped cream	

In a mixing bowl, combine all ingredients except unbeaten egg white. Stir until smooth with a wooden spoon. Lightly brush pie shell with egg white and fill shell with pumpkin mixture. Bake 55-60 minutes at 400 F (200 C). Pie is done when a sharp knife inserted, comes out clean. Cool. Serve topped with whipped cream. 6 servings.

"He went into the pantry and smelled the fruit cakes that lay on the inverted pans they'd been cooked in."
Ernest Buckler, **Anticipation.**

PUMPKIN CREAM PIE

1-16 oz	can pumpkin	398 mL
1/2 cup	sugar	125 mL
1/2 tsp	salt	2 mL
1/2 tsp	cinnamon	2 mL
1/2 tsp	nutmeg, grated	2 mL
1/2 tsp	cloves	2 mL
1/2 tsp	ginger	2 mL
1	envelope gelatine, unflavoured	
1/4 cup	orange juice	50 mL
1 pt	vanilla ice cream	500 mL
1-9"	pie shell, baked	1 L
	whipped cream, whipped	
	Mandarin oranges, drained	

In a saucepan, combine pumpkin, sugar, salt and spices and heat. Stir in gelatine, dissolved in orange juice. Remove from heat and cool to room temperature. Soften ice cream and beat smooth with beaters or a food processor. Add to cooled pumpkin mixture and blend thoroughly. Pour mixture into baked pie shell and refrigerate, at least 2 hours. Garnish with whipped cream and Mandarin oranges.

NO-BAKE PUMPKIN PIE

1	envelope gelatine, unflavoured	
1 tsp	cinnamon	5 mL
1/2 tsp	ginger	2 mL
1/2 tsp	nutmeg, ground	2 mL
1/2 tsp	salt	2 mL
1-14 oz	can Eagle Brand Sweetened Condensed Milk (NOT evaporated milk)	300 mL
2	eggs	
1-14 oz	can pumpkin	398 mL
1-9"	graham cracker crumb crust 1 L	

In a heavy saucepan, combine gelatine, spices and salt. Stir in Sweetened Condensed Milk and eggs and mix well. Let stand 1 minutes. Over low heat, cook and stir constantly until gelatine dissolves and mixture thickens slightly about 10 minutes. Remove from heat. Stir in pumpkin until thoroughly mixed. Pour into pie crust. Refrigerate 3 hours or until set. 6-8 servings.

SPIRITED EGG NOG CUSTARD PIE

1-9″	pie shell, unbaked	1 L
1-14 oz	can Eagle Brand Sweeteened Condensed Milk (NOT evaporated milk)	300 mL
1 1/3 cups	warm water	325 mL
2 tbsp	light Rum	30 mL
1 tbsp	Brandy	15 mL
1 tsp	vanilla extract	5 mL
1/2 tsp	nutmeg, ground	2 mL
3	eggs, well beaten	

To ensure pie shell doesn't shrink, prick bottom and sides with a fork, and line pastry with foil. Fill with dry beans. Bake 8 minutes at 425 F (218 C). Remove foil and beans. In a large mixing bowl, combine all ingredients except eggs and mix well. Stir in eggs. Pour into prepared pie shell and bake 10 minutes at 425 F (218 C). Reduce oven temperature to 325 F (160 C) and continue baking 25-30 minutes. Knife inserted in centre should come out clean. Cool. Chill if desired.

FROZEN CRANBERRY VELVET PIE

1 1/4 cups	vanilla wafer crumbs	300 mL
6 tbsp	butter, melted	90 mL
1-8 oz	package cream cheese	250 g
1 cup	whipping cream	250 mL
1/4 cup	sugar	50 mL
1/2 tsp	vanilla	2 mL
1-16 oz	can whole cranberry sauce	500 g
	whipping cream, whipped	

In a bowl, combine crumbs and melted butter and press into a 9″ (1 L) pie plate. Chill until firm. In a mixing bowl, beat cream cheese until fluffy. In another bowl, combine whipping cream, sugar, and vanilla and whip until thickened but not stiff. Gradually add to creamed cheese until mixture is smooth and creamy. Fold in cranberry sauce, reserving a few whole berries for the top. Spoon into crust and freeze until firm. Remove from freezer 10 minutes before serving. Top with whipped cream and garnish with reserved cranberries. Serves 8-10.

"As the Christmas-tide drew near, milk was unfrozen for the mixing of pies, cakes, custards and coquignoles . . ."
Corinne Rocheleau Rouleau, **When Heaven Smiled On Our World**

CRANBERRY CRUMB PIE

1	deep dish pie shell, unbaked	
1-8 oz	package cream cheese	250 g
1-14 oz	can Eagle Brand Sweetened Condensed Milk (NOT evaporated milk)	300 mL
1/4 cup	ReaLemon lemon juice from concentrate	50 mL
3 tbsp	light brown sugar	5 mL
2 tbsp	cornstarch	30 mL
1-14 oz	can whole cranberry sauce	398 mL
1/4 cup	butter, cold	50 mL
1/3 cup	flour	75 mL
3/4 cup	walnuts, chopped	175 mL

To ensure pie shell doesn't shrink, prick bottom and sides with a fork, and line pastry with foil. Fill with dry beans. Bake 8 minutes at 425 F (218 C). Remove foil and beans. In a large mixing bowl, beat cheese until fluffy. Gradually beat in Sweetened Condensed Milk until smooth. Stir in ReaLemon. Pour mixture into prepared pie shell. In a small bowl, combine 1 tbsp (15 mL) sugar and cornstarch. Stir in cranberry sauce. Spoon evenly over cheese mixture. In a mixing bowl, cut butter into flour and remaining 2 tbsp (30 mL) sugar until crumbly. Stir in nuts. Sprinkle evenly over cranberry mixture. Bake 45-50 minutes at 375 F (190 C), until bubbly and golden. Cool. Serve at room temperature or chilled. 6-8 servings.

CRANBERRY PIE

1-3 oz	lemon jello	85 g
1 cup	boiling water	250 mL
2 cups	fresh cranberries	500 mL
1/2 cup	water	125 mL
1/2 cup	sugar	125 mL
2 cups	Cool Whip	500 mL
1-9″	pie shell, baked (crumb crust	1 L

Dissolve lemon jello in boiling water. In a saucepan, combine cranberries and water and cook until skins burst. Add sugar and cook 5 more minutes. Drain juice from cranberries and add juice to gelatin mixture. Chill until thickened. Combine cranberries, Cool Whip, and gelatine mixture. Chill until partially set. Pour mixture into pie shell and refrigerate until serving. 6 servings.

"Now plums and spice, sugar and honey, square it among pies a broth"
Washington Irving, The Christmas Coach

CHERRY CHEESE PIE

1-9″	graham cracker crumb crust	1 L
1-8 oz	package cream cheese	250 g
1-14 oz	can Eagle Brand Sweetened Condensed Milk (NOT evaporated milk)	300 mL
1/3 cup	ReaLemon lemon juice from concentrate	75 mL
1 tsp	vanilla extract	5 mL
	cherry pie filling, chilled	

In a large mixing bowl, beat cheese until fluffy. Beat in Sweetened Condensed Milk until smooth. Stir in ReaLemon and vanilla. Pour into crumb crust and chill about 3 hours or until set. Top with the desired amount of pie filling before serving. 6-8 servings.

CHRISTMAS SNOW PIE

1	envelope gelatine, unflavoured	
1 tsp	gelatine, unflavoured	5 mL
1/4 cup	water, cold	50 mL
1/4 cup	sugar	50 mL
1/4 cup	flour, sifted	50 mL
1/2 tsp	salt	2 mL
1 1/2 cups	milk	375 mL
1 1/2 cups	whipping cream	375 mL
1/4 cup	sugar	50 mL
1 tsp	vanilla	5 mL
1/4 tsp	almond extract	1 mL
1/2 cup	mixed candied peel, chopped	125 mL
3 1/2 oz	coconut, flaked	89 g
1-9″	pie shell, baked	1 L

Soften gelatine in cold water. In a saucepan, combine 1/4 cup (50 mL) sugar, flour, and salt. Add milk gradually and cook until thick, stirring continuously. Remove from heat and stir in gelatine until thoroughly mixed. Chill until mixture begins to set. In a mixing bowl, beat cream and add 1/4 cup (50 mL) sugar. In a separate bowl, beat gelatine mixture until smooth. Stir in vanilla, almond and peel. Fold in whipped cream and 3/4 of coconut. Garnish with remaining coconut. Chill overnight. 6-8 servings.

"Little Jack Horner sat in the corner,
Eating a Christmas pie:
He put in his thumb, and pulled out a plum,
And Said, "What a good boy am I!"
  "Little Jack Horner"

PECAN TARTS

1 cup	corn syrup	250 mL
2/3 cup	brown sugar	150 mL
1/4 cup	butter	50 mL
2	eggs, beaten	
1/4 tsp	salt	1 mL
1/2 tsp	vanilla	2 mL
2/3 cup	pecans, chopped	150 mL
	tart shells, unbaked	
	pecans, whole	

In a saucepan, combine corn syrup and brown sugar and cook 5 minutes. Pour syrup mixture over beaten eggs. Add remaining ingredients and blend well. Fill tart shells and top each with one whole pecan. Bake for 15-20 minutes at 350 F (180 C). Makes about 2 dozen tarts.

OLD-FASHIONED BUTTER TARTS

1 cup	brown sugar	250 mL
1/4 cup	butter	50 mL
2	eggs	
1/2 cup	coconut, desiccated	125 mL
3 tbsp	milk (cream)	4 mL
	raspberry jam (optional)	
	tart shells, unbaked	

In a mixing bowl, or food processor, combine all ingredients. Fill each tart shell with a spoonfull of raspberry jam and then fill 3/4 full with brown sugar mixture. Bake 20 minutes at 350 F (180 C). Filling can be refrigerated until use and kept for several weeks. Makes about 2 dozen tarts.

MINI FRUIT CHEESE TARTS

1-8oz	package cream cheese	250 g
1-14 oz	can Eagle Brand Sweetened Condensed Milk (NOT evaporated milk)	300 mL
1/3 cup	ReaLemon lemon juice from concentrate	75 mL
1 tsp	vanilla	5 mL
	assorted fruit (strawberries, blueberries, bananas, raspberries, orange segments, cherries, kiwifruit, etc.)	
1/4 cup	apple jelly, melted	50 mL
	tart shells, baked	

MINI FRUIT CHEESE TARTS cont.

In a large mixing bowl, beat cheese until fluffy. Gradually beat in Sweetened Condensed Milk until smooth. Stir in ReaLemon and vanilla. Spoon into tart shells. Top with fruit and brush with melted jelly. Chill thoroughly. Makes about 2 dozen tarts.

FROZEN EGG NOG TARTS

1	envelope gelatine, unflavoured	
1/4 cup	water	50 mL
3	eggs, separated	
1-14 oz	can Eagle Brand Sweetened Condensed Milk (NOT evaporated milk)	300 mL
2 tbsp	Brandy	30 mL
2 tbsp	light Rum	30 mL
1 cup	whipping cream, whipped	250 mL
48-2″ or 3″	tart shells, baked (graham cracker crumb crust)	48-5 or 7 cm
	whipping cream, whipped	
	nutmeg, grated	

In a small saucepan, sprinkle gelatine over water. Let stand 1 minute. Stir over low heat until gelatine is dissolved, about 5 minutes. Remove from heat. In a mixing bowl, beat egg yolks and stir in condensed milk, gelatine, Brandy and Rum. In another mixing bowl, beat egg whites until stiff. Fold egg whites and whipped cream into gelatine mixture. Fill tart shells 3/4 full and freeze about 4 hours or until firm. Garnish with whipped cream and nutmeg. Makes about 48 tarts.

"Christmas Day has always been flavoured to me with the pound cake and apple-jelly tarts of those first days in Manitoba."
   Nellie McClung

NEW YORK SQUARES

bottom layer

1/2 cup	butter	125 mL
1/4 cup	sugar	50 mL
1/3 cup	cocoa	75 mL
1 tsp	vanilla	5 mL
1	egg, beaten	
1 cup	coconut, desiccated	250 mL
1 3/4 cups	graham wafer crumbs	425 mL
1/2 cup	walnuts, chopped	125 mL

filling

1/4 cup	butter	50 mL
2 tbsp	custard powder	25 mL
2 tbsp	milk	25 mL
2 cups	icing sugar, sifted	500 mL

top layer

2-1 oz	squares, semi-sweet chocolate	2-28 g
1 tbsp	butter	15 mL

In the top part of a double boiler, cook butter, sugar, cocoa, vanilla and egg until thick. Remove from heat and stir in coconut, crumbs and walnuts. Pat firmly into a greased 9″ (2.5 L) square pan. Chill for about 1 hour. In a mixing bowl, cream butter, custard powder and milk. Gradually beat in icing sugar. Spread over first layer in pan. Chill until firm. In a saucepan, heat chocolate and butter, stirring until melted. Drizzle chocolate over cream filling. Refrigerate until serving. Makes about 30 squares.

LEMON SQUARES

crust

1 cup	brown sugar	250 mL
1 cup	butter	250 mL
1 cup	flour	250 mL
1 cup	coconut	250 mL
14	soda crackers, crumbed	
1 tbsp	vanilla	1 mL

LEMON SQUARES cont.

filling

1 cup	sugar	250 mL
1 cup	water, cold	250 mL
1	egg	
1	lemon, juice only	
1/2 cup	butter	125 mL
2 tbsp	cornstarch	30 mL

In a mixing bowl, thoroughly combine all ingredients. Place half the mixture in a 12 x 8 x 2″ (2.5 L) pan. In the top part of a double boiler, combine filling ingredients and cook until thick. Spread on crust and top with remaining crust mixture. Bake 30-40 minutes at 325 F (160 C).

APPLESAUCE FRUITCAKE BARS

1-14 oz	can Eagle Brand Sweetened Condensed Milk (NOT evaporated milk)	300 mL
2	eggs	
1/4 cup	butter, melted	50 mL
2 tsps	vanilla	10 mL
3 cups	biscuit mix	750 mL
2 cups	jar applesauce	500 mL
1 cup	dates, chopped	250 mL
3/4 cup	green glacécherries, chopped	175 mL
3/4 cup	red glacé cherries, chopped	175 mL
3/4 cup	nuts, chopped	175 mL
3/4 cup	raisins	175 mL
	icing sugar	

In a large mixing bowl, beat Sweetened Condensed Milk, eggs, butter and vanilla. Stir in remaining ingredients except confectioners' sugar. Spread evenly into a well-greased and floured 15 x 10″ (2 L) jellyroll pan. Bake 35-40 minutes at 325 F (160 C). Cool thoroughly. Sprinkle with icing sugar and cut into bars. Store at room temperature. Makes about 48 bars.

" . . .and if the cook do not lack wit, he will sweetley lick his fingers."
Washington Irving, **The Christmas Coach**

CLASSIC BROWNIES

1 cup	shortening	250 mL
1 1/2 cups	brown sugar	375 mL
2	eggs	
1 1/8 cups	flour	275 mL
3/4 tsp	baking powder	3 mL
1/4 tsp	salt	1 mL
4 1/2 tbsp	cocoa	65 mL
3/4 tsp	vanilla	3 mL
1/2-1 cup	walnuts, chopped	125-250 mL

In a saucepan, melt shortening. In a mixing bowl, combine all ingredients with shortening. Pour batter into a 13 x 9 x 2" (2.5 L) pan and bake 15 minutes at 400 F (200 C). Reduce heat to 350 F (160 C) and bake 5 minutes longer. Cool and top with icing.

icing

1 1/2 cups	icing sugar	375 mL
2 1/2 tbsp	cocoa	35 mL
3 tbsp	butter	45 mL
2 1/2 tbsp	milk	35 mL
pinch	vanilla	

In a mixing bowl, combine icing sugar and cocoa. Cut in butter and add milk. Add vanilla and stir.

ALMOND SQUARES

1 1/2 cups	pastry flour	375 mL
1/4 tsp	salt	1 mL
1/2 cup	sugar	125 mL
1/2 cup	butter	125 mL
2	egg whites	
1 cup	brown sugar	250 mL
1/4 tsp	salt	1 mL
1/2 tsp	vanilla	2 mL
1/4 cup	almonds	50 mL

In a mixing bowl, sift in dry ingredients and cut in butter. Crumble with fingers and pat mixture into an 8" (2 L) square pan. In a bowl, beat egg whites until stiff. Add sugar, salt, vanilla, and spread over crust. Sprinkle almonds on top and bake 45 minutes at 350 F (180 C). Cool before cutting.

Nut cakes originated in Spain and Italy.

APRICOT BARS

2/3 cup	dried apricots	150 mL
	water	
1/2 cup	butter, softened	125 mL
1/4 cup	sugar	50 mL
1 cup	flour, sifted	250 mL
1/3 cup	flour, sifted	75 mL
1/2 tsp	baking powder	2 mL
1/4 tsp	salt	1 mL
1 cup	brown sugar	250 mL
2	eggs, well beated	
1/2 tsp	vanilla	2 mL
1/2 cup	nuts, chopped	125 mL

In a saucepan, boil apricots in enough water to cover them, for 10 minutes. Drain, cool, and chop in pieces. In a mixing bowl, combine butter, sugar and 1 cup (250 mL) flour until crumbly. Pat into an 8″ (2 L) square pan and bake 25 minutes at 350 F (180 C) until lightly browned. In a mixing bowl, sift in 1/3 cup (75 mL) flour, baking powder, and salt. Beat in brown sugar and eggs. Add vanilla, nuts, and apricots. Spread mixture over baked layer and bake 30 minutes at 350 F (180 C). Cool and cut in bars. Makes about 2 1/2 dozen squares.

CHINESE CHEWS

2	eggs	
2/3 cup	sugar	150 mL
2/3 cup	flour, sifted	150 mL
1 tsp	baking powder	5 mL
1/4 tsp	salt	1 ml
1 tsp	vanilla	5 mL
1/2 cup	dates, chopped	125 mL
1/2 cup	raisins	125 mL
3/4 cup	walnuts, chopped	175 mL
	sugar (icing sugar)	

In a mixing bowl, beat eggs until foamy and add sugar. Sift in dry ingredients and mix well. Add flavouring, fruit, and nuts, and mix by hand. Spread mixture evenly in a greased 8″ (2 L) square pan. Bake 30 minutes at 350 F (180 C). Cut in bars and roll in sugar while still warm.

MOM'S PINEAPPLE DESSERT

2 cups	milk	500 mL
1 cup	sugar	250 mL
2	egg yokes	2
1	lemon jello	85 g
2	egg whites	2
1-14 oz	can crushed pineapple, drained	398 mL
2 cups	whipping cream, whipped	500 mL
1	large angel food cake, cut in 4 layers	
1/2 cup	whipping cream, whipped	125 mL
1/2 cup	coconut, toasted	125 mL

In the top part of a double boiler, cook milk, sugar and egg yokes until thick. Add lemon jello and stir until dissolved. Cool mixture until partially set. Fold in beaten egg whites, pineapple, and whipped cream. Cut angel cake in layers, making the bottom layer a thin one. Place the top layer in a tube pan. Add a layer of filling. Alternate cake and filling, ending with the thin, bottom cake layer. Refrigerate until cake is firmly set. Remove from tube pan. Garnish with whipping cream and toasted coconut.

PINEAPPLE DESSERT

crust

1	box vanilla crackers (save 1/4 cup (50 mL) for top)	
1/2 cup	butter, melted	125 mL

Combine ingredients and press into an 12″ X 8″ (28 X 18 cm.) rectangular pan. Bake at 350 F. (180 C) for 15 minutes. Cool.

filling

1/2 cup	butter, melted	12 mL
1 1/2 cups	icing sugar	375 mL
2	eggs	
1/2 tsp	vanilla	2 mL

Combine ingredients and beat well until smooth. Spread on crumb crust.

top layer

1 cup	whipping cream, whipped (save portion for top)	250 mL
1-20 oz	crushed pineapple, drained	625 mL

Fold cream and pineapple together. Spread on filling. Top with remaining whipped cream and sprinkle with 1/4 cup (50 mL) cracker crumbs. Chill and serve.

FROZEN PUMPKIN BOMBE

layer 1

2 1/2 cups	gingersnap crumbs	625 mL
1/4 cup	sugar	50 mL
1/4 cup	butter, melted	50 mL

layer 2

2 pts	vanilla ice cream, softened	1 L

layer 3

1-19 oz	can pumpkin	540 mL
1 cup	sugar	250 mL
1/2 tsp	salt	2 mL
1 tsp	cinnamon	5 mL
1/2 tsp	ginger	2 mL
1/4 tsp	cloves	1 mL
1 cup	whipping cream, whipped	250 mL
1 tsp	vanilla	5 mL

Grease a 2 1/2 qt (2.5 L) mixing bowl. Line bowl with a sheet of buttered foil. Combine crumbs, sugar and butter. Reserve 1/2 cup (125 mL) for the top. Press the remainder into the bottom and up the sides of the lined bowl and place in the freezer. When crumb crust is frozen, press the softened ice cream into the bottom and up the sides of the bowl. Freeze again. In a mixing bowl combine all ingredients except whipped cream. Fold in whipped cream to pumpkin mixture. Pour over the frozen ice cream layer. Top with crumbs and freeze again. Invert and unmould bombe on a serving platter. Cover with plastic wrap and keep frozen until serving.

PUMPKIN RUM CUSTARDS

1 cup	sugar	250 mL
4	eggs	
1-14 oz	can Eagle Brand Sweetened Condensed Milk (NOT evaporated milk)	300 mL
1 1/2 cups	water	375 mL
1-14 oz	can pumpkin	398 mL
1/3 cup	light Rum	75 mL
1/2 tsp	nutmeg, ground	2 mL
1/2 tsp	salt	2 ml
1/4 tsp	ginger	1 mL

PUMPKIN RUM CUSTARDS cont.

In a heavy skillet, over medium heat, cook sugar, stirring constantly until melted and caramel-coloured. Using 8-10 custard cups, pour about 1 tbsp (15 mL) carmelized sugar on bottom of each. In a large mixing bowl, beat eggs and stir in remaining ingredients. Pour equal portions of mixture into prepared cups. Set cups in shallow pan. Fill pan with 1″ (2.5 cm) hot water. Bake 50-60 minutes at 350 F (180 C). Cool and chill thoroughly. Invert custards onto serving plate. 8-10 servings.

EGG NOG DESSERT

4 oz	mixed fruit and peel	125 g
3 tbsp	white Rum	45 mL
1 qt	egg nog	1 L
1/4 cup	corn starch	50 mL
1/2 cup	whipping cream, whipped	125 mL

In a mixing bowl, combine mixed fruit and peel with Rum. Cover and leave standing at room temperature. In a saucepan, thicken egg nog with cornstarch. Fold in fruit and whipped cream. Chill and serve in a bowl or individual serving dishes.

APRICOT AMBROISA

1-28 oz	can apricot halves, drained	796 mL
1-14 oz	can Eagle Brand Sweetened Condensed Milk (NOT evaporated milk)	300 mL
1/3 cup	ReaLemon lemon juice from concentrate	75 mL
1 cup	can crushed pineapple, drained	250 mL
1/2 cup	almonds, slivered, tosted, chopped	125 mL
1 cup	whipping cream, whipped	250 mL
1 1/3 cups	coconut, flaked, toasted	325 mL

Chop 6 apricot halves for garnish and set aside. In a blender or a food processor, blend remaining apricots until smooth. In a large bowl, combine Sweetened Condensed Milk, ReaLemon, pineapple and pureed apricots. Fold in almonds and whipped cream. In each individual serving dish, layer 2 tsps (10 mL) coconut, 1/2 cup (125 mL) apricot mixture, and top with reserved apricots and 2 tsps (10 mL) toasted coconut. Chill 2 hours or until set. Can be prepared in one serving dish.

CRANBERRY DELIGHT

1-16 oz	can cranberry sauce	500 g
3 tbsp	ReaLemon lemon juice from concentrate	45 mL
1 cup	whipped cream	250 mL
1/4 cup	icing sugar	50 mL
1/4 cup	mayonnaise	50 mL
1 cup	walnuts, chopped	250 mL

In a mixing bowl, combine cranberry sauce and ReaLemon. Place in individual cups or a serving dish. Blend remaining ingredients and pour over cranberry mixture. Chill and serve.

FIG SOUFFLE

3 cups	figs, chopped	750 mL
2 tbsp	sugar	30 mL
4 tbsp	Brandy	60 mL
4	egg whites, stiffly beaten	
pinch	salt	
1/2 tsp	ReaLemon lemon juice from concentrate	2 mL
3 tbsp	almonds, shredded	45 mL
1/2 cup	whipped cream, whipped	125 mL
1 tbsp	Brandy	15 mL

In a saucepan, heat chopped figs with sugar and Brandy until barely warm. Remove from heat and fold in stiff egg whites, salt, and ReaLemon. Butter a 1 qt (1 L) soufflé dish. Sprinkle dish with almonds and pour in fig mixture. Bake 30 minutes at 375 F (190 C), until puffy and golden. Serve at once with whipped cream which has been flavoured with 1 tbsp Brandy. 6 servings.

In Armenia, a young man gives his sweetheart 12 pieces of cake, one for each month of the year, as a symbol that he can provide for her.

FROZEN MOCHA CHEESECAKE

1 1/4 cups	chocolate wafer cookie crumbs	300 mL
1/4 cup	butter, melted	50 mL
1/4 cup	sugar	50 mL
1-8 oz	package cream cheese	125 g
1-14 oz	can Eagle Brand Sweetened Condensed Milk (NOT evaporated milk)	300 mL
2/3 cup	chocolate syrup	150 mL
1-2 tbsp	instant coffee	15-30 mL
1 tsp	hot water	5 mL
1 cup	whipping cream, whipped	250 mL
	chocolate wafer crumbs	

Combine crumbs, butter and sugar and press firmly on the bottom and side of a 9″ (22.5 cm) spring form pan. In a mixing bowl, beat cheese until fluffy. Gradually beat in Sweetened Condensed Milk and chocolate syrup until smooth. In small bowl, dissolve coffee in water. Add to cheese mixture and mix well. Fold in whipped cream and pour mixture into prepared pan. Cover and freeze 6 hours or overnight. Garnish with chocolate crumbs.

NANCY'S ROYAL CHERRY CHEESE CAKE

1	package chocolate wafers	
1-19 oz	can cherry pie filling	540 mL
1/2 cup	butter, melted	125 mL
1-8 oz	package cream cheese	250 g
1 cup	icing sugar	250 mL
2 cups	Cool Whip	500 mL
1 tsp	vanilla	5 mL

Reserve 12 whole wafers for edge of cheese cake. Crush remaining wafers and reserve some crumbs for top. In a bowl, combine crumbs and butter and press into a 9″ (22.5 cm) spring form pan. Stand up whole wafers around edge of pan and bake 15 minutes at 300 F (150 C). Cool and pour pie filling on crumb crust. In a mixing bowl, combine cheese, icing sugar, Cool Whip, and vanilla until well blended. Pour over pie filing. Sprinkle with crumbs and refrigerate for several hours or overnight.

The poinsettia is a Mexican plant popularized in the United States and Canada in 1828 by Dr. Poinsett.

On facing page: **Chocolate Chip Cheesecake** (bottom), page 145, and **No-Bake Chocolate Cheesecake**, page 145.

CHOCOLATE CHIP CHEESECAKE

1 1/2 cups	creme-filled chocolate sandwich cookies, finely crushed	375 mL
2-3 tbsp	butter, melted	30-45 mL
3-8 oz	packages cream cheese	3-250 g
1-14 oz	can Eagle Brand Sweetened Condensed Milk (NOT evaporated milk)	300 mL
3	eggs	
2 tsps	vanilla	10 mL
1 cup	mini chocolate chips	250 mL
1 tsp	flour	5 mL

In a bowl, combine cookie crumbs and butter and press firmly on the bottom of a 9″ (22.5 cm) spring form pan. In a mixing bowl, beat cheese until fluffy. Gradually beat in Sweetened Condensed Milk until smooth. Add eggs and vanilla and mix well. In a small bowl, toss 1/2 cup (125 mL) chips with flour to coat; stir into cheese mixture and pour into prepared pan. Sprinkle remaining chips evenly over top. Bake 1 hour or until cake springs back when lightly touched. Cool to room temperature and refrigerate. Serve chilled.

NO-BAKE CHOCOLATE CHEESECAKE

1/3 cup	butter, melted	75 mL
1 1/4 cups	graham cracker crumbs	300 mL
1/4 cup	sugar	50 mL
1	envelope gelatine, unflavoured	
2/3 cup	water	
1-8 oz	packages cream cheese	2-250 g
4-1 oz	squares semi-sweet chocolate, melted	4-28 g
1-14 oz	can Eagle Brand Sweetened Condensed Milk (NOT evaporated milk)	300 mL
1 tsp	vanilla	5 mL
1 cup	whipping cream, whipped	250 mL

In a bowl, combine butter, crumbs and sugar. Press firmly on bottom of a 9″ (22.5 cm) spring form pan. In a small saucepan, sprinkle gelatine over water. Let stand 1 minute. Over low heat, stir until gelatine dissolves; set aside. In a large mixing bowl, beat cheese and chocolate until fluffy. Gradually beat in Sweetened Condensed Milk and vanilla until smooth. Stir in gelatine mixture. Fold in whipped cream. Pour into prepared pan. Chill 3 hours or until set. May be garnished with whipped cream and melted chocolate.

MINCEMEAT DESSERT

2 cups	gingersnap crumbs	500 mL
1/3 cup	butter, melted	75 mL
1 1/2 tbsp	gelatine, unflavoured	7 mL
5 tbsp	water, cold	75 mL
2 cups	mincemeat	500 mL
4	eggs, separated	
1/4 cup	butter	50 mL
1/2 cup	ReaLemon lemon juice from concentrate	125 mL
1/2 cup	sugar	125 mL
1 cup	whipping cream, whipped	250 mL

In a bowl, combine crumbs and melted butter. Mix thoroughly and pat all but 1/2 cup (125 mL) into a 13 x 9 x 2″ (2.5 L) pan. Refrigerate. Soften gelatine in cold water. In a large saucepan, combine mincemeat, slightly beaten egg yokes, butter and ReaLemon and heat until thick (about 15 minutes), stirring constantly. Remove from heat and add gelatine stirring until dissolved. Refrigerate. When mincemeat mixture begins to firm, prepare a soft meringue of beaten egg whites and sugar. Fold meringue and whipped cream into mincemeat mixture. Pour into prepared pan and sprinkle with remaining crumbs. Chill for several hours. 12-15 servings.

CHERYL'S TRIFLE

1	day old white cake	1
	Brandy to taste	
4 cups	mixed fruit (fruit cocktail, peaches, bananas, Mandarin oranges etc.)	1 L
	slivered almonds to taste	
3/4 cup	sugar	175 mL
2 tbsp	cornstarch	30 mL
1 cup	milk and cream mixture (half and half)	250 mL
4	egg yolks, well beaten	4
2 tbsp	butter	30 mL
1 1/2 tsp	vanilla	7 mL
1 cup	whipping cream, whipped	250 mL

In a tall bowl, place a layer of cut-up cake in the bottom and sprinkle with Brandy. Add a layer of mixed fruit. Top with almonds. In the top part of a double boiler, combine sugar and cornstarch. Slowly add milk and cream mixture. Cover and cook without stirring for 10 minutes. Uncover and cook another 10 minutes stirring frequently. Add egg yolk, and butter and cook while stirring for 2 minutes. Allow

CHERYL'S TRIFLE cont.

mixture to cool on its own, stirring occasionally. Once cool, add vanilla and fold in whipped cream. Chill. Custard mixture should be the consistency of heavy cream. Add a layer of custard to ingredients in bowl. Repeat layers of cake, Brandy, fruit, almonds, and custard several times, ending with a custard layer. Sprinkled with almonds. Chill and serve.

PEACH MELBA TRIFLE

1-14 oz	can Eagle Brand Sweetened Condensed Milk (NOT evaporated milk)	300 mL
1 1/2 cups	water	375 mL
1-3 3/4 oz	package instant vanilla pudding	92 g
2 cups	whipping cream, whipped	500 mL
1/4 cup	Sherry (orange juice)	50 mL
1 tbsp	Sherry (orange juice)	15 mL
1-10 oz	package angel food cake, torn in pieces	400 g
1 1/2 lbs	peaches, fresh, pared, sliced	750 g
	OR	
1-28 oz	can sliced peaches, drained	796 mL
1/4 cup	red raspberry preserves (jam)	50 mL
	almonds, toasted	

In a large bowl, combine Sweetened Condensed Milk and water and mix well. Add pudding mix and beat until well blended. Chill 5 minutes. Fold in whipped cream and sherry. Place 4 cups(1 L) cake pieces in a glass serving bowl. Sprinkle with 2 tbsp (30 mL) orange juice. Top with half the peaches and 1/4 cup (50 mL) preserves and half the pudding mixture. Repeat layering with remaining cake, sherry, peaches, and pudding. Chill. Garnish with almonds. 12 servings.

FRUIT SALAD

1 cup	sour cream	250 mL
1 cup	miniature marshmallows	250 mL
1 cup	coconut	250 mL
1 cup	Mandarin oranges, drained	250 mL
1 cup	pineapple chunks, drained	250 mL
1/2 cup	Maraschino cherries	125 mL
1 tbsp	sugar	15 mL

In a mixing bowl, combine all ingredients. Refrigerate until serving. 10 servings.

CURRIED FRUIT

1-14 oz	can pears, drained	398 mL
1-14 oz	can peaches, drained	398 mL
1-14 oz	can pineapple tid bits, drained	398 mL
1/2 cup	figs (optional)	250 mL
1 tsp	curry powder	5 mL
1 tsp	cinnamon	5 mL
1 tsp	nutmeg, grated	5 mL
	butter	

In a mixing bowl, combine all fruit. Place in a casserole dish. Sprinkle fruit with spices and dot with butter. Bake 30 minutes at 325 F(160 C) and serve hot. 6-8 servings.

COCONUT MACAROONS

2	packages flaked coconut	2-200 g
1-14 oz	can Eagle Brand Sweetened Condensed Milk (NOT evaporated milk)	300 mL
2 tsps	vanilla	10 mL
1 1/2 tsps	almond extract	7 mL

In a large mixing bowl, combine coconut, Sweetened Condensed Milk and extracts. Mix well. Drop by rounded spoonfuls onto aluminum foil-lined and generously greased baking sheets. Bake 8-10 minutes or until lightly browned around edges. Remove IMMEDIATELY from baking sheets. Store at room temperature. 4 dozen cookies.

MOM'S SHORT BREAD COOKIES

1/2 lb	butter	250 g
1/2 cup	sugar	125 mL
1/2 cup	cornstarch	125 mL
1 1/2 cups	flour	375 mL
1 tbsp	vanilla	15 mL
	cherries, chopped	

In a mixing bowl, cream butter and add remaining ingredients. Blend until smooth. Drop batter from a spoon onto a lightly greased cookie sheet or use batter through a cookie press. Bake 20-25 minutes at 325 F (160 C), until delicate golden brown. Garnish with cherry pieces.

HOLIDAY THIMBLE COOKIES

1 cup	butter	250 mL
1/4 cup	brown sugar	50 mL
1	egg yolk	
1 1/2 cups flour	375 mL	
1	egg white	
1 cup	walnuts, finely chopped	250 mL
	jam (jelly)	

In a mixing bowl, cream butter and sugar. Beat in egg yolk and combine with flour. Form batter into balls and dip each ball in beaten egg white. Roll each ball in walnuts and place on a greased cookie sheet. Press a hollow into each ball with a thimble. Bake for 5 minutes at 325 F (160 C). Press hollow again with thimble and bake another 15-20 minutes until cookies are lightly browned. Cool and fill hollow with jam.

ALMOND COOKIES

6 tbsp	butter	90 mL
1 cup	brown sugar	250 mL
1/4 cup	water, cold	50 mL
1 3/4 cups	flour, sifted	425 mL
1 tsp	soda	5 mL
1/2 tsp	salt	2 mL
1/2 tsp	cinnamon	2 mL
1/2 cup	almonds, blanched, slivered	125 mL

In a mixing bowl, cream butter and sugar. Add water. Sift in dry ingredients and add almonds, stirring by hand. Form batter into a roll, 2 1/2" (6 cm) in diameter. Cut batter in 1/8" (.4 cm) thick slices. Bake 6-8 minutes at 400 F ((200 F). 4 dozen cookies.

ALMOND STAR COOKIES

1 cup	butter, softened	250 mL
1 1/4 cups	sugar	300 mL
1/4 tsp	almond extract	1 mL
1 1/4 cups	almonds with skins, finely ground	300 mL
pinch	salt	
1 3/4 cups	flour	400 mL
	confectioners' sugar	

In a mixing bowl, cream butter. Add granulated sugar gradually and beat until light. Add flavouring and stir in nuts, salt, and flour. Roll out dough, a small amount at a time, on a well-floured board to less than 1/8″ (.4 cm) thickness. Cut with floured star-shaped cutter. Bake 8-10 minutes at 325 F (160 C). Cool on racks and dust with confectioners' sugar. Store in airtight container.

OLD-FASHIONED BRANDY SNAPS

2/3 cup	butter	150 mL
1/3 cup	brown sugar	150 mL
4 oz	corn syrup	125 mL
1 tsp	ginger	5 mL
1/2 tsp	nutmeg, grated	2 mL
1 cup	flour	250 mL
1 tsp	brandy	5 mL
	whipped cream	
	candied ginger	

In a saucepan, melt butter. Add sugar, syrup, and ginger and remove from heat. Sift in flour and nutmeg. Add brandy and stir. Drop batter from a spoon onto a greased cookie sheet and bake 10-15 minutes at 400 F (200 C). Lift cookies from baking sheet and roll each around the handle of a wooden mixing spoon to form tubes or cones. Reheat cookies if they harden before being rolled. Fill with whipped cream and candied ginger just before serving.

The Christmas tree custom was introduced into England when Queen Victoria married German Prince Albert. Early emigrants from England and Germany introduced the custom to the Americas.

WINE DROP COOKIES

1/2 cup	shortening	125 mL
1 1/4 cups	sugar	300 mL
2	eggs	
1/2 cup	Port wine	125 mL
2 3/4 cup	flour	675 mL
1/4 tsp	salt	1 mL
1/2 tsp	baking soda	2 mL
1/2 tsp	baking powder	2 mL
1 cup	raisins	250 mL
1 cup	dates, chopped	250 mL

In a mixing bowl, cream shortening and sugar. Add eggs one at a time and beat well after each. Stir in Port. Sift dry ingredients twice and add to batter. Blend in raisins and nuts and combine thoroughly. Drop batter from a spoon onto an ungreased cookie sheet and bake 8-10 minutes at 375 F (190 C), until lightly browned. 4 dozen cookies.

KRINGEL

3	hard boiled egg yolks	
1	raw egg yolk	
1/2 cup	sugar	125 mL
3 tbsp	butter	45 mL
4 tbsp	shortening	60 mL
2 cups	flour	500 mL
1/2 tsp	cinnamon	2 mL
1 tsp	peel, finely chopped	5 mL
1 1/2 tsp	vanilla	7 mL
	egg white	
	walnuts	

In a blender or food processor, chop hard boiled egg yolks. In a mixing bowl, cream sugar, butter, and shortening and add egg yolks. Add remaining ingredients and form batter into a smooth ball. Chill at least 2 hours. Place batter between 2 pieces of waxed paper and roll to 1/8" (.4 cm) thick. Cut batter with doughnut cutter and place on a greased cookie sheet. Paint each cookie with egg white and decorate with walnuts. Bake 8-10 minutes at 350 F (180 C). 3 dozen cookies.

Santa Claus is known in other parts of the world as Kris Kringle, St. Nicholas, La Befana, Yule Tomten, Christkindli, and Papa Noel.

TRADITIONAL BROWN CHRISTMAS COOKIES

1/2 cup	dark corn syrup	125 mL
1/2 cup	molasses	125 mL
1/4 cup	butter, melted	50 mL
1/2 cup	brown sugar	125 mL
2 1/2 cups	flour	625 mL
pinch	salt	
1/2 tbsp	ginger	2 mL
1/4 tsp	cloves	1 mL
1/2 tsp	cinnamon	2 ml
1/2 tsp	soda	
1 1/2 tsp	vinegar	7 mL

In the top part of a double boiler, warm syrup, molasses, and butter. Stir in sugar. Sift in flour, salt, and spices and stir well. Add soda-vinegar mixture and refrigerate batter at least 2 hours, until stiff. Place batter on a lightly floured board and roll paper thin. Cut into shapes and bake 6 minutes at 375 F (190 C). 3 1/2 dozen cookies.

SWEDISH GINGER COOKIES

1/2 cup	butter	125 mL
1/2 cup	sugar	125 mL
1/4 cup	molasses	50 mL
1	egg	
1 1/2 cups	flour, sifted	375 mL
1/2 tbsp	ginger	7 mL
1 tsp	cinnamon	5 mL
1/2 tsp	cloves	2 mL
1/4 tsp	allspice	1 mL
1/4 tsp	nutmeg, grated	1 mL
1/2 tsp	baking soda	2 mL

In a mixing bowl, cream butter and sugar. Add molasses and egg. Sift in dry ingredients and blend thoroughly. Wrap batter in waxed paper and chill overnight. Roll out a small amount of batter at one time. Cut into shapes and bake 8-10 minutes at 350 F (180 C). 4 dozen cookies.

Martin Luther is said to have introduced the practice of lighting the Christmas tree with candles.

GINGERBREAD COOKIES

1/2 cup	shortening	125 mL
1/2 cup	molasses	125 mL
1/2 cup	sugar	125 mL
1	egg	
3 1/4 cups	flour, sifted	750 mL
2 tsp	baking soda	10 mL
1/2 tsp	salt	2 mL
1 1/2 tsp	ginger	7 mL
1 tsp	cinnamon	5 mL
	raisins, cherries	

In a saucepan, melt shortening and cool. In a mixing bowl, combine shortening, molasses, sugar, and egg and beat well. Sift in dry ingredients. Wrap batter in waxed paper and refrigerate overnight. Roll out on lightly floured board to 1/4″ (.75 cm) thickness. Cut in shapes and decorate with raisins or cherries and bake 10-12 minutes at 375 F (190 C).

GINGER SNAPS

3/4 cup	shortening	175 mL
1 cup	sugar	250 mL
1	egg, unbeaten	
1/4 cup	molasses	50 mL
2 cups	flour, sifted	500 mL
1 1/2 tsps	soda	7 mL
1 tsp	cloves	5 mL
1 tsp	cinnamon	5 mL
1 tsp	ginger	5 mL

In a mixing bowl, cream shortening and add sugar. Add egg and molasses and beat until smooth. Sift in remaining dry ingredients and blend thoroughly. Drop batter from a spoon onto a cookie sheet and bake 16 minutes at 350 F (180 C). 4 dozen cookies.

GERMAN SPICE COOKIES

4 cups	flour, sifted	1 L
2 tsp	baking powder	10 mL
1 cup	sugar	250 mL
1/2 tsp	coriander	2 mL
1 tsp	cinnamon	5 mL
1 tsp	cloves	5 mL
1/2 tsp	nutmeg	2 mL
1/4 tsp	cardamon	1 mL
1	egg	
2 tsp	vanilla	10 mL
3 tbsp	milk	45 mL
3/4 cup	butter	175 mL
1/2 cup	almonds, ground (hazelnuts)	125 mL

In a mixing bowl, sift in flour and baking powder. Add sugar, spices, egg, vanilla, and milk. Stir well and cut in butter. Add nuts and more flour if batter is not a manageable dough. Form batter into a ball and refrigerate at least 2 hours. Turn onto a lightly floured board and roll 1/8" (.4 cm) in thickness. Cut into shapes and place on a greased cookie sheet. Bake 7-8 minutes at 400 F (200 C). 5 dozen cookies.

CUT-OUT COOKIES

3 cups	all-purpose flour	750 mL
1 tbsp	baking powder	15 mL
1/2 tsp	salt	2 mL
1-14 oz	can Eagle Brand Sweetened Condensed Milk (NOT evaporated milk)	300 mL
3/4 cup	butter, softened	175 mL
2	eggs	
2 tsps	vanilla	10 mL
	frosting	

In a large mixing bowl, combine flour, baking powder and salt and set aside. In another mixing bowl, beat Sweetened Condensed Milk, butter, eggs, and vanilla until well blended. Add dry ingredients and mix well. On a floured surface, lightly knead dough to form a smooth ball. Divide into thirds. On a well-floured surface, roll out each portion to 1/8" (4 mm) thickness. Cut with floured cookie cutter. Place 1" (2.5 cm) apart on a greased cookie sheet. Bake at 350 F (180 C) 7-9 minutes or until lightly browned around the edges. Cool thoroughly. Frost and decorate. Store at room temperature. 6 1/2 dozen cookies.

Christmas day, 1735, Paul Revere was born.

MINCEMEAT COOKIES

1/4 cup	shortening	50 mL
1/2 cup	sugar	125 mL
1	egg, beaten	
1 cup	mincemeat	250 mL
1 1/4 cups	flour	300 mL
1 1/2 tsp	baking powder	7 mL
1/8 tsp	salt	0.5 mL

In a mixing bowl, cream shortening and sugar together. Add egg and mincemeat. Sift in dry ingredients. Drop batter from a spoon onto a greased cookie sheet. Bake 12 minutes at 375 F (190 C). 3 dozen cookies.

MINCE-OATMEAL COOKIES

1/2 cup	mincemeat, drained	125 mL
1/2 cup	water	
1/4 cup	shortening	50 mL
1/4 cup	sugar	50 mL
1	egg	
1 1/2 cups	rolled oats	375 mL
1/2 cup	flour, sifted	125 mL
1/2 tsp	soda	2 mL
1/4 tsp	salt	1 mL
1/2 tsp	cinnamon	2 mL
1/4 tsp	nutmeg, grated	1 mL

In a saucepan, cook mincemeat and water until thickened and cool. In a mixing bowl, cream shortening and sugar and beat in egg. Add mincemeat and rolled oats. Sift in dry ingredients and combine thoroughly. Drop batter from a spoon onto a greased cookie sheet. Bake 10-12 minutes at 375 F (190 C), until lightly browned.

"Busier than an English oven at Christmas", is an Italian metaphor!

CHRISTMAS HERMITS

3/4 cup	shortening	175 mL
1 cup	brown sugar	250 mL
3	eggs, beaten	
2 1/2 cups	cake flour, sifted	625 mL
3/4 tsp	baking soda	3 mL
1/2 tsp	salt	2 mL
1/2 cup	sultana raisins	125 mL
1/2 cup	walnuts, chopped	125 mL
1/4 cup	cherries, red glazed	50 mL
1/4 cup	cherries, green glazed	50 mL

In a mixing bowl, cream shortening and sugar and add eggs. Sift dry ingredients together and dust fruit and nuts with 1/2 the flour mixture. Add other 1/2 of flour mixture to creamed ingredients. Fold in fruit and nuts and stir well. Drop batter from a spoon onto a greased cookie sheet. Bake 10 minutes at 350 F (180 C). 7 dozen cookies.

CHRISTMAS EVE DROP COOKIES

1 cup	brown sugar	250 mL
1/4 cup	shortening	50 mL
1	egg, beaten	
1/4 tsp	vanilla	1 mL
1 cup	flour, sifted	250 mL
1 tsp	baking powder	5 mL
1/4 cup	dates, chopped	50 mL
1/4 cup	almonds, blanched, chopped	50 mL
1/8 cup	candied cherries	30 mL

In a mixing bowl, cream brown sugar and shortening. Add egg and vanilla and beat well. Sift in dry ingredients. Stir in dates, almonds and cherries. Drop by teaspoonfuls on a buttered cookie sheet. Preheat oven to 400 F (200 C), then reduce heat to 350 F (180 C) and bake 7-10 minutes.

NANA MAC'S CHRISTMAS FRUIT ROLL

2	squares semi-sweet chocolate	2
2	squares unsweetened chocolate	2
2 tbsp	butter	30 mL
1	egg	
1 1/2 cups	icing sugar	375 mL
1 cup	chopped walnuts	250 mL
2 cups	marshmallows, quartered (coloured or white)	500 mL
1 cup	dates, chopped	250 mL
1 cup	Marachino cherries, chopped	250 mL
3/4 cup	graham cracker crumbs	175 mL

In the top part of a double boiler, melt chocolate and butter. Beat in egg. Remove from heat and add icing sugar, walnuts, marshmallows, dates, and cherries. Chill and then roll mixture into a long cylinder shape. Roll in graham cracker crumbs. Refrigerate. Slice to serve.

STRAWBERRY BON BONS

1-14 oz	can Eagle Brand Sweetened Condensed Milk (NOT evaporated milk)	300 mL
2	packages flaked coconut	200 g
1-6 oz	package strawberry jello	170 g
1 cup	almonds, blanched, ground	250 mL
1 tsp	almond extract	5 mL
	red food colouring	
2 1/4 cups	confectioners' sugar, sifted	550 mL
3 tbsp	whipping cream	45 mL
	green food colouring	

In a large bowl, combine Sweetened Condensed Milk, coconut, 1/3 cup (75 mL) gelatine, almonds, extract and enough red food colouring to tint mixture a strawberry shade. Chill 1 hour or until firm enough to handle. Using about 2 tsp (10 mL) for each, form into strawberry shapes. Sprinkle remaining gelatine onto wax paper. Roll each strawberry in gelatin to coat. Place on wax paper-lined baking sheets and chill. In a small bowl, combine sugar, cream and green food colouring. Using pastry bag with open star tip, pipe small amount on each strawberry. Cover and store at room temperature or refrigerate. 5 dozen bon bons.

CHOCOLATE AMARETTO BALLS

3-6 oz	packages semi-sweet chocolate chips	3-175 g
1-14 oz	can Eagle Brand Sweetened Condensed Milk (NOT evaporated milk)	300 mL
3 tbsp	Amaretto liqueur	45 mL
1/2 tsp	almond extract	2 mL
	almonds, finely chopped	

In a heavy saucepan, over low heat, melt morsels with Sweetened Condensed Milk and remove from heat. Stir in Amaretto and extract and chill 2 hours. Shape into 3/4″ (2 cm) balls and roll in nuts. Chill until firm. Store at room temperature in a tightly covered container. Flavour improves after 24 hours. 6 dozen balls.

RUM BALLS

2 cups	vanilla wafer crumbs	500 mL
1 cup	icing sugar	250 mL
3/4 cup	pecans, finely chopped	175 mL
2 tbsp	cocoa	30 mL
2 tbsp	corn syrup	30 mL
1/3 cup	Rum	75 mL
	icing sugar	

In a mixing bowl, combine all ingredients thoroughly. Shape into balls and roll in icing sugar. Refrigerate. Store 2 days before using. 4 dozen balls.

COCONUT RUM BALLS

2 2/3 cups	package vanilla wafer crumbs	650 mL
1 cup	nuts, finely chopped	250 mL
1 1/3 cups	flaked coconut	325 mL
1-14 oz	can Eagle Brand Sweetened Condensed Milk (NOT evaporated milk)	300 mL
1/4 cup	Rum	50 mL
	icing sugar (flaked coconut)	

In a large bowl, combine crumbs, nuts, and coconut. Add Sweetened Condensed Milk and Rum and mix well. Chill 4 hours. Dip hands in confectioners' sugar and shape mixture into 1″ (2.5 cm) balls. Roll in icing sugar. Rechill if mixture becomes too soft. Refrigerate. 5 dozen balls.

SHERRY PECAN BALLS

3 cups	vanilla wafer crumbs	750 mL
1 cup	pecans, ground	250 mL
1 cup	icing sugar	250 mL
3 tbsp	corn syrup	45 mL
1 3/4 tbsp	cocoa	25 mL
1/2 cup	Sherry	125 mL
1/4 cup	icing sugar, sifted	50 mL

In a mixing bowl, blend all ingredients except 1/4 cup (50 mL) sifted icing sugar. Shape into balls and roll in icing sugar. Refrigerate until serving. 3 dozen balls.

SNOWBALLS

4 tbsp	sugar	60 mL
1/4 tsp	salt	1 mL
1/2 cup	butter	125 mL
1 cup	flour, sifted	250 mL
1 tbsp	Rum	15 mL
1 cup	pecans, chopped	250 mL
	icing sugar	

In a bowl, combine sugar, salt, and butter and set aside. In a mixing bowl, combine flour, Rum and pecans, and then add sugar mixture. Form into balls and bake on a cookie sheet for 20 minutes at 325 F (160 C). While still hot, dip in icing sugar. Cool and roll in sugar. 2 1/2 dozen balls.

PEANUT BUTTER BALLS

1 cup	peanut butter	250 mL
1 cup	dates, chopped	250 mL
1/2 cup	walnuts, chopped	125 mL
1 cup	icing sugar	250 mL
2 cups	icing sugar	500 mL
2 tbsp	butter	30 mL
	milk	
	coconut	

In a mixing bowl, combine peanut butter, chopped dates, walnuts and icing sugar. Form into bite-sized balls. In another bowl, make icing with sugar, butter and milk. Icing should be runny. Dip each ball in icing and then coconut. Refrigerate until using. Keep a very long time. 3 dozen balls.

SHARON'S POTATO BALLS

1/2 cup	potatoes, cooked and mashed	125 mL
2-3 cups	coconut, dessicated	500-750 mL
2-3 cups	icing sugar	500-750 mL
	red and green food colouring	
2-1 oz	squares semi-sweet chocolate, melted	2-28 g

In a mixing bowl, combine potatoes, coconut and icing sugar. Divide batter into three portions. Leave one portion white; tint one portion with red food colouring and the other with green. Form into balls. Dip the bottom of each ball in melted chocolate. Cool. 2 dozen balls.

CHOCOLATE TREATS

1 cup	peanut butter	250 mL
1 cup	icing sugar	250 mL
1 tbsp	butter, softened	15 mL
1/2 cup	dates, chopped	125 mL
1/2 cup	cherries, chopped	125 mL
1/2 cup	almonds, slivered	125 mL
4-1 oz	squares semi-sweet chocolate, melted	4-28 g

In a mixing bowl, cream peanut butter, icing sugar and butter. Stir in fruits and nuts and shape into balls. Chill. Dip balls into melted chocolate. Refrigerate until serving. 3 dozen balls.

CHOCOLATE TRUFFLES

3-6 oz	packages semi-sweet chocolate chips	3-175 g
1-14 oz	can Eagle Brand Sweetened Condensed Milk (NOT evaporated milk)	300 mL
1 tbsp	vanilla extract	15 mL
	nuts, finely chopped	
	coconut, flaked	

In a heavy saucepan, over low heat, melt chips with Sweetened Condensed Milk. Remove from heat and stir in vanilla. Chill 2 hours or until firm. Shape into 1" (2.5 cm) balls and roll in nuts or coconut. Chill 1 hour. Store at room temperature. 6 dozen balls.

FONDANT

1/3 cup	butter, softened	75 mL
1/3 cup	corn syrup	75 mL
1/2 tsp	salt	2 mL
1 tsp	vanilla extract	5 mL
3 1/2 cups	icing sugar, sifted	875 mL

In a mixing bowl, blend all ingredients well. Form into shapes and serve.
1 1/2 lbs (750 g).

FOOLPROOF CHOCOLATE FUDGE

3-6 oz	packages semi-sweet chocolate chips	3-175 g
1-14 oz	can Eagle Brand Sweetened Condensed Milk (NOT evaporated milk)	300 mL
pinch	salt	
1 1/2 tsps	vanilla	7 mL
1/2 cup	nuts, chopped (optional)	125 mL

In a heavy saucepan, over low heat, melt chips with Sweetened Condensed Milk.
Remove from heat and stir in remaining ingredients. Spread evenly into wax
paper-lined 8″ (2 L) square pan. Chill 2-3 hours until firm. Turn fudge onto cutting
board and remove paper. Cut in squares and store at room temperature. Makes
about 1 3/4 lb (1 Kg).

LAYERED MINT CHOCOLATE CANDY

1-12 oz	package semi-sweet chocolate chips	350 g
1-14 oz	can Eagle Brand Sweetened Condensed Milk (NOT evaporated milk)	300 mL
2 tsps	vanilla extract	10 mL
6 oz	white confectioners' coating (also known as white chocolate)	175 mL
1 tbsp	peppermint extract green food colouring	15 mL

In a heavy saucepan, over low heat, melt chips with 1 cup (250 mL) Sweetened
Condensed Milk. Stir in vanilla. Spread half the mixture into wax paper-lined 8″
(2 L) square pan. Chill 10 minutes or until firm. Keep remaining chocolate mixture
at room temperature. In a heavy saucepan, over low heat, melt coating with
remaining Sweetened Condensed Milk. Stir in peppermint extract and food colouring if desired. Spread on chilled chocolate layer and chill 10 minutes or until
firm. Spread reserved chocolate mixture on mint layer. Chill 2 hours or until firm.
Turn onto cutting board and remove paper. Cut into squares and store at room
temperature. Makes about 1 3/4 lb (1 kg).

MARZIPAN

1/2 cup	almonds, blanched, whole, finely ground	125 mL
1/2 cup	sugar	125 mL
1	egg white, beaten	
1 cup	icing sugar, sifted	250 mL
	ReaLemon lemon juice from concentrate	

In a mixing bowl, combine almonds and sugar to form a soft paste. Blend with fluffy egg white. Add icing sugar and ReaLemon, and mix until smooth. Add icing sugar and enough ReaLemon to obtain a dough-like consistency. Knead until smooth and form into various shapes. Marzipan may be coloured, dipped in chocolate, seeds, nuts, and fruit.

MALLOW PECAN ROLL

1-7 1/2 oz	jar marshmallow cream	200 g
3 1/2 cups	icing sugar	875 mL
1 tsp	vanilla	5 mL
1/4 tsp	almond extract	1 mL
1 lb	caramels	500 g
10 cups	pecans	1.25 L

In a mixing bowl, combine marshmallow, sugar and extracts. Shape into 8 rolls 1″ (2.5 cm) in diameter. Place rolls in freezer until very hard. In the top part of a double boiler, melt caramels. Dip the rolls in caramel until coated and then roll in pecans. Press pecans into the caramel, cool, and store in a dry place. 5 lbs (2.5 kg).

"Of course there were sweets. It was the marshmallows that squelched. Hardboileds, toffee, fudge and allsorts, crunches, cracknels, humbugs, glaciers and marzipan and butterwelsh for the Welsh."
Dylan Thomas, **Conversation About Christmas**

EASY HOMEMADE CHOCOLATE ICE CREAM

1-14 oz	can Eagle Brand Sweetened Condensed Milk (NOT evaporated milk)	300 mL
2/3 cup	chocolate syrup	150 mL
2 cups	whipping cream, whipped	500 mL

In a large bowl, stir together Sweetened Condensed Milk and syrup. Fold in whipped cream. Pour into a foil-lined 9 x 5" (1 L) loaf pan. Cover and freeze 6 hours or until firm. Scoop ice cream from pan or remove from pan, peel off foil and slice.

FRENCH VANILLA ICE CREAM

1-14 oz	can Eagle Brand Sweetened Condensed Milk (NOT evaporated milk)	300 mL
2 tbsp	water	30 mL
3	egg yolks, beaten	
4 tsp	vanilla	20 mL

In a large bowl, combine Sweetened Condensed Milk, water, egg yolks and vanilla. Fold in whipped cream.

MINT CHOCOLATE ICE CREAM

1-14 oz	can Eagle Brand Sweetened Condensed Milk (NOT evaporated milk)	300 mL
2 tsp	peppermint extract	10 mL
4 drops	green food colouring	
4 tsp	vanilla	20 mL
1/2 cup	mini chocolate chips	125 mL

In a large bowl, combine Sweetened Condensed Milk, peppermint, food colouring and water. Fold in whipped cream and baking chips.

COFFEE ICE CREAM

1-14 oz	can Eagle Brand Sweetened Condensed Milk (NOT evaporated milk)	300 mL
1 tbsp	instant coffee	15 mL
2 tbsp	water	30 mL
2	egg yolks, beaten	
4 tsp	vanilla	

Dissolve coffee in water. In a large bowl, combine Sweetened Condensed Milk, coffee mixture, egg yolks and vanilla. Fold in whipped cream.

Happy Blendings

FUDGY MILK CHOCOLATE FONDUE

1-10 oz	can chocolate syrup	284 mL
1-14 oz	can Eagle Brand Sweetened Condensed Milk	300 mL
	(NOT evaporated milk)	
pinch	salt	
1 1/2 tsp	vanilla	

In a heavy saucepan, combine syrup, Sweetened Condensed Milk and salt. Over medium heat, cook and stir 12-15 minutes or until slightly thickened. Remove from heat. Stir in vanilla. Serve warm with fruit pieces or cubed pound cake for dipping.

RICH CHOCOLATE SAUCE

8-1 oz	squares of semi-sweet chocolate	8-28 g
2-1 oz	squares unsweetened chocolate	2-28 g
1/2 cup	sugar	125 mL
1/2 cup	water	125 mL
1 tsp	butter	5 mL
3 tbsp	heavy cream	45 mL

In the top part of a double boiler, heat chocolate, sugar and water until blended. Add butter and cream and mix well. Serve hot, cold, or at room temperature over ice cream or cake. 6 servings.

SAUCE FOR CHRISTMAS PUDDING

3 tbsp	butter	45 mL
1 cup	icing sugar	250 mL
2	egg yolks	
1/2 cup	milk	125 mL
1 tsp	vanilla	5 mL
1 cup	whipping cream, whipped	250 mL

In the top part of a double boiler, combine butter, icing sugar, egg yolks, and milk and cook until mixture coats a spoon. Add vanilla and cool. Fold in whipped cream and serve. 6-8 servings.

RUM SAUCE

2 tbsp	sugar	30 mL
2 tsp	cornstarch	10 mL
1/4 tsp	cinnamon	1 mL
2 tbsp	water	30 mL
1/2 cup	Rum	125 mL
1 tbsp	coconut, grated	15 mL

In a saucepan, combine sugar, cornstarch, and cinnamon. Add water and rum. Cook until thickened, stirring constantly. Stir in coconut and serve hot. 4-6 servings.

HARD SAUCE

1 cup	brown sugar	250 mL
2 1/2 tbsp	flour	45 mL
2 tbsp	butter	30 mL
	boiling water	
1/2 tsp	salt	2 mL
1/2 tsp	nutmeg, grated	2 mL
1/2 tsp	vanilla	2 mL

In a saucepan, thoroughly blend sugar and flour. Add butter and enough boiling water to make a paste. Cook until thickened. Add more water or flour to obtain a thick consistency. Add nutmeg, salt and vanilla. Serve hot. 4-6 servings.

MINCEMEAT SAUCE

1/4 cup	Brandy	50 mL
8 oz	mincemeat	250 g

In a saucepan, heat mincemat. Add Brandy and serve hot. 8–10 servings.

RUM BUTTER SAUCE

2 oz	butter	60 mL
4 oz	brown sugar	125 mL
	nutmeg, grated	
2 tbsp	Rum	30 mL

In a bowl, cream butter and sugar. Add nutmeg and Rum and beat well. Refrigerate and serve cold.

JACKIE'S RUM POT

1 lb	each fruit of the season	500 g

(strawberries, wash, remove stems, halve; raspberries and blackberries, DO NOT WASH; apricots, peaches, scalded 2 minutes, peeled, pitted, and quartered; plums, washed, stemmed, pitted; grapes (seedless), washed, stemmed; cherries, washed, stemmed, pitted; red currants, washed, stemmed; melons, peeled, seeded, cubed; pears, washed, sliced, simmered in water and sugar 4 minutes; pineapple, peeled, cored, cubed.

1/2 cup	sugar	125 mL
	light amber Rum	

In a crock or rumtopf, place 1 lb (500 g) of strawberries (this should be your first fruit). Cover with sugar and let stand 1 hour. Cover with light amber Rum so all fruit is submerged. Seal crock with cellophane so alcohol won't escape. Place a loose-fitting lid on top. As each fruit comes in season, add it to the crock using the same proportions of fruit, sugar, and Rum. Pineapple should be the last fruit added. Do not stir. Store in a cool place. Do not refrigerate. Contents will be ready 3 months after last fruit is added. Serve over ice cream, custards, and cake. May also be used in baking.

PEANUT BUTTER SAUCE

1-14 oz	can Eagle Brand Sweetened Condensed Milk	300 mL
	(NOT evaporated milk)	
1/3 cup	peanut butter	75 mL
	peanuts, chopped (optional)	

In a heavy saucepan, over low heat, combine Sweetened Condensed Milk and peanut butter. Cook and stir until well blended. Stir in peanuts. Serve warm or cold. 1 1/2 cups (375 mL).

PECAN RUM SAUCE

1/4 cup	butter	50 mL
1-14 oz	can Eagle Brand Sweetened Condensed Milk	300 mL
	(NOT evaporated milk)	
1/2 tsp	Rum flavouring	2 mL
pinch	salt	
1/4 cup	pecans, chopped	50 mL

In a small saucepan, over medium heat, melt butter and add remaining ingredients. Cook and stir until thickened, 10-12 minutes. Serve warm. 1 1/2 cups (375 mL).

ALMOND PASTE ICING

1 cup	icing sugar	250 mL
1 cup	sugar, fine	250 mL
2 cups	almonds, blanched, finely chopped	500 mL
3	egg yolks, beaten	
1 tsp	ReaLemon lemon juice from concentrate	5 mL
1/2 tsp	almond extract	2 mL
	egg white, slightly beaten	

In a mixing bowl, sift in sugars and stir in almonds. In a separate bowl, combine juice, extract, and beaten egg yolks. Combine all ingredients. Mixture should be the consistency of dough for kneading. Add ReaLemon if too crumbly or icing sugar if too runny. Knead until smooth on a board sprinkled with icing sugar. Roll icing between two pieces of waxed paper until thin. Cut icing in one piece to fit cake. Moisten cold cake with egg white that has been slightly beaten and top with icing. Press into place. Christmas cake that is to be topped with royal icing should be stored for several days first.

ROYAL ICING

2	egg whites	
pinch	salt	
3-3 1/2 cups	icing sugar	875 mL
1 tsp	ReaLemon lemon juice from concentrate	2 mL
1 tsp	rosewater (glycerin)	5 mL

In a mixing bowl, beat egg whites and salt until thick. Add sugar, juice, and rosewater, until mixture forms stiff peaks. Icing should be the consistency of stiff paste. Adjust the amount of icing sugar or ReaLemon to achieve paste. Apply icing in thin layers, allowing each layer to dry before applying the next. Royal icing is to be applied over almond paste icing on fruit cake.

MARZIPAN FROSTING

1 cup	almonds, blanched and unblanched	250 mL
4 cups	icing sugar	1 L
3	egg whites	
1 tsp	almond extract	5 mL

Purée almonds in electric blender or food processor. Add sugar and continue blending. In another bowl, beat egg whites until fluffy and add to almond mixture. Mix in extract. Frost Christmas cakes and breads.

SPICE CAKE ICING

6 tbsp	butter, softened	90 mL
8 tbsp	icing sugar	125 mL
4 tsp	milk	20 mL
4 tsp	water	20 mL

In a bowl, cream butter and sugar. Add milk and water and beat thoroughly.

BROWN SUGAR ICING

1/4 cup	butter, softened	50 mL
3/4 cup	brown sugar	175 mL
4 tbsp	cream	60 mL
1/3 cup	coconut	75 mL

In a bowl, cream butter, sugar, and cream. Stir in coconut. Ice cake and place under the broiler for 2-3 minutes until icing bubbles.

LIGHT ICING

2	egg whites	
1/2 cup	sugar	125 mL
1 tsp	vanilla	5 mL
pinch	salt	
2 tbsp	cold water	30 mL

In the top part of a double boiler, beat all ingredients until well blended, about 3 minutes. Cool and top cool cakes.

LEMON GLAZE

5/8 cup	icing sugar	150 mL
1/8 cup	ReaLemon lemon juice from concentrate (orange juice)	25 mL
1/2 tsp	vanilla	2 mL

In a bowl, combine ingredients and blend until smooth. Glaze cakes and cookies.

HONEY GLAZE

1/2 cup	sugar	125 mL
1/4 cup	milk	50 mL
1/4 cup	butter	50 mL
1/4 cup	honey	50 mL
1/2 cup	walnuts, crushed	125 mL

In a saucepan, combine all ingredients and bring to a boil. Spread on coffee cakes before baking.

MAYONNAISE

1-14 oz	can Eagle Brand Sweetened Condensed Milk (NOT evaporated milk)	300 mL
1/3 cup	white vinegar	75 mL
2 tbsp	mustard	30 mL

Thoroughly combine all ingredients. Place in a sterile jar and keep refrigerated.

SANDWICH SPREAD

1/2 cup	butter	125 mL
3 tsp	mustard	15 mL
3	eggs, well beaten	
1 cup	sugar	250 mL
1 tsp	salt	5 mL
1/4 lb	Cheddar cheese, grated	125 g
1/2 cup	cream	125 mL
3	green peppers, finely chopped	
3	red pepper, finely chopped	
3/4 cup	vinegar	175 mL
1/4 cup	water	50 mL

In the top part of a double boiler, combine butter, mustard, eggs, sugar and salt and cook until thickened. Let cool. Add remaining ingredients and cook 5 more minutes.

ABBREVIATIONS

cm   centimetres
C   degrees Centigrade
F   degrees Fahrenheit
g   grams(s)
hr   hour(s)
kg   kilogram(s)
lb   pound(s)
L   litre(s)
min   minute(s)
mL   millilitre(s)
mm   millimetre(s)
no   number
oz   ounce(s)
pt   pint(s)
qt   quart(s)
tbsp   tablespoon(s)
tsp   teaspoon(s)
"   inch(es)
( )   alternative ingredient

STANDARD MEASURES

pinch = less than 1/8 tsp
3 tsp = 1 tbsp
4 tbsp = 1/4 cup
16 tbsp = 1 cup
1 cup = 1/2 pt
2 cups = 1 pt

CONTENT OF CANS

can size	average content	servings
no 300	1 3/4 cups (425 mL)	3–4
1 tall	2 cups (500 mL)	4
no 303	2 cups (500 mL)	4
no 2	2 1/4 cups (550 mL)	4–5
no 2 1/2	3 1/2 cups (875 mL)	6–7
no 3	4 cups (1 L)	8
no 10	12–13 cups (3 L)	24

INDEX

E

F

G

H

I